THE FAMILY GUARESCHI

The Family Guareschi

Chronicles of the Past and Present

Giovanni Guareschi

G 914

TRANSLATED BY L. K. CONRAD

FARRAR, STRAUS AND GIROUX NEW YORK

Contents

Part Two · Stories About Jo

Part One

From Teacher to Pupil

Dear Teacher...

Dear Teacher,

I have exciting news for you. Ten minutes ago what you were waiting for came—your Certificate. It's beautiful, your Certificate. It's printed on a large piece of very white paper; the text is written in a fancy script and there are numerous capital letters radiating ornate curlicues. On top is the seal of the Republic of Italy with its cogged wheel and its white star, not to mention the laurel and oak branches. It reads:

The President of the Republic
under the Bill of April 26, 1928, Article 12, Section 97
through the Good Offices of the Minister of Public Education
Decrees
that this Honorary Certificate shall be bestowed upon you and
that on presentation of it to the authorities you will receive
the Gold Medal of Honor
for having completed forty years of good service in the Public
Elementary Schools.

It also says that:

The abovementioned Minister is placed in charge of carrying
out this Decree.

At the bottom left there's a nice blind stamping. Just to the right of that is written:

Signed Luigi Einaudi
Witness Gonella

The *Signed* and the *Witness* are printed. Naturally the signatures are handwritten. Otherwise they wouldn't be signatures. However, unlike the Chief of District's signature, which appears at the very foot of the page in a completely illegible scrawl, the signatures of President Einaudi and Minister Gonella are clear as day, inscribed in the same calligraphic script as the date and other variables inserted on the document.

It's not that the President of the Republic and the Minister of Public Education have precisely the same handwriting and that one or the other of them drew up the document. Actually the work was done by a scribe whose sole job is to fill out documents of this nature. We all know how many hundreds of thousands of old teachers go on pension every year. It's not humanly possible for a President of a Republic or his Minister to set aside twenty hours per day to sign retirement certificates. In any case all that matters is that the original of the document is signed, never mind the copy they send out to the retiring teachers. The original must be properly signed, because otherwise how would you be able to collect your Gold Medal of Honor?

I know what you're going to say. Your good service amounted to forty-nine years, not forty. Now you know perfectly well that a Minister of Public Education who has so much to do for his Party, and a President of the Republic who has so many worries, can't stand on one foot waiting to check if an ancient schoolteacher has the right to a Gold Medal of Honor based on forty-nine or fifty years of good service, rather than just forty.

Anyhow, what's nine years?

That dry, terse "good service" puts you off? What would you have chosen instead, "praiseworthy service"? A President of a Republic and his Minister can't put themselves on the line with overspecific phraseology, you know that. Furthermore, they can't go through the process of checking whether the service of a teacher has been "praiseworthy" or "mediocre" or "excellent" as opposed to "good." Don't lose sight of the forest by crabbing about the trees, dear teacher. Just bear in mind the overall gist. The State is awarding you the kudos you deserve after forty-nine years of hard work and is sending you, completely free of charge, a document which, given the thickness of the paper and the quality of the ink, can't have cost them less than twelve lire.

I wish you could see how handsome it is, your Certificate.

It's dated "Rome, December 22, 1949" and arrived here October 17, 1950, a mere ten months later.

But you, dear teacher, are dead. You left us on the 13th of July and you never got to see your Certificate. Why are retired teachers always so impatient?

It's a shame, though. If the Certificate had come just a few months sooner, I'd have bought you a pretty gold medal to pin on your blouse and you might have been able to take your gold medal on the long trip with you. But how can one do that sort of thing without benefit of a Certificate? It's absolutely essential, that document.

But Rome's a long way from Milan, and for a Certificate

to arrive it can't take less then ten months. And they're so busy, down there at the Ministry.

Now what am I going to do with this Certificate? Should I keep it? But does the law allow keeping something that doesn't belong to one? Shall I send it back to Minister Gonella? And what does Minister Gonella know about old retired teachers who haven't the patience to wait ten months? In fact, what is it about teachers that makes them die just as soon as they retire? What am I going to do with this Certificate? Should I send it back to the Ministry of Public Education? What if they take offense? "We put a lot of work into that document, in fact a lot of research, and you're sending it back?" What if they write me that, what can I answer?

I suppose I can put it on your grave on All Souls' Day. The seal is sturdy and so is the paper. However, the ink in which your name and other details are written is insubstantial. A bit of dew or rain and the whole lot would be washed away. Even the date, December 22, 1949. And I need to see it in writing, that date. You taught us about life and death but I'm your worst pupil. That's because I'm your Frati, the one who always made his mother cry. I need to see that date in writing, see it every day, because my heart is full of poison and I need to hate those faceless men and federal sloths that deprived you of the joy that might have given you the strength to keep going one day longer, or one hour or one minute.

Now don't start thrashing around in your grave, don't disturb your eternal cold—I know, dear teacher, to you everything federal was sacred and what I'm saying is a horrible sacrilege to you. But I'm not speaking for you alone.

I'm exuding poison for myself and for all the people whose last days were soured by appalling federal sloth and deaf bureaucratic indifference.

As for you, you half-baked petty functionaries who take ten months to get a Certificate of Merit from Rome to Milan, one day you will find yourselves old and miserable and the State will put you out on your ears too, and then you'll understand the value of a piece of paper like the one that came to me today. Maybe then I'll stop hating you.

But until that day I will hate you tenaciously. Even if you stole a single second from my mother's life, even if you stole only one smile from her lips.

I'm an inconsequential man, but my hatred is as immense as the love I bore my mother. So warm yourselves in the Roman sunshine while ignoring this man exuding poison in the northern fogs—one day the Roman sun won't come out to warm your shattered old bones and then this inconsequential man's hatred will weigh on your shoulders like a sack of wet sand.

You say you're underpaid? So was my mother, and yet she never tired of her work.

Don't be upset, dear teacher, they can't do anything to me. My hatred is stronger than all the Ministers and Presidents put together. Just talk to me, if you can, while I'm asleep. But please don't come just to complain that what I've said isn't worthy of a noble soul. My hatred doesn't seek vengeance. It is, and always will be, simply a thought closed up inside my brain. And please don't come with stories about loving my neighbors as I love myself. You taught me all about that. I love myself only when I know I've done what, according to your teachings and your example, I thought was my duty. When I know I haven't, then I hate myself.

I'll have the Certificate framed and hang it on the wall above my work table. From time to time I'll look at it.

Until I have in my eyes a little of that light you gave me, taking advantage of a day of vacation, I am

Your Son.

White Wine

They had come from a long way off, from a village on the other side of the mountain, and they already had walked forty kilometers or more, cutting across fields along the naked rows of vines, for the traffic and the infernal racket and stink of the cars confused them.

They stepped weightlessly on the dead leaves, tiny shadows wandering through the vast, still darkness of the autumn night. Once they reached the Valley sunk in sleep, they emerged from the fields to continue their journey along the highway. Soon the wind cleared away the clouds and the moon shone bright as a street lamp. Flanked by tall hedges that made the muddy strip seem narrower than it was, the narrow road suddenly gave way into a large square farmyard. One side of it opened on the highway and the other three were hemmed in by new buildings painted white with green shutters, the walls decorated with brick colonettes, plinths, architraves, and cornices.

The old man came to a halt. "Here we are," he said. "This is his place."

"How do you know?" the old woman growled.

"Only an idiot like him could sink money into land that

one clearly couldn't squeeze a lira out of and then build on it stables, siloes, farmhouses etc. etc. Not a whit of common sense."

"Shut up," the old woman hissed. "You're one to talk, after ruining yourself buying acre after acre and building like a lunatic and then selling the lot, without getting back so much as the cost of the weeds that covered the vegetable garden."

"It was a promising venture," the old man cried. "Was it my fault the government put in crop restrictions?"

"When everything went up in smoke," the old woman went on unappeased, "we were left without a straw. You even sold the beds and we had to sleep on mattresses thrown on the floor."

"Bankruptcy is a disaster for everybody, creditors and debtors alike. Not just the creditors, the way it was in the good old days."

"In the good old days?" the old woman shrieked. "As for example the time I came home from the shore with the children to find the house empty—apart from china and linen scattered around—after you'd sold all the furniture?"

"I always bought more furniture," the old man defended himself.

"Which was never paid for, so they were always back to repossess it."

"If you'd kept an eye on things instead of always being wrapped up in that confounded school of yours," the old man shouted, "things might have gone a little better."

"If I hadn't had my pittance of a salary and that house my parents left me," she snapped back, "where would we be now?"

"Precisely where we are," the old man retorted, giggling.

Their quarrel had taken them into the farmyard and the old man wanted to inspect the machine shed. (Agricultural machinery, the smell of lubricating oil and gasoline, were catnip to the old man.) "Look at this!" he exclaimed indignantly. "Just look at the crust on this tractor! And this hay baler! And this reaper! Mud, rust, pieces falling off and tacked back on with wire, dried-up oil filters. People who mistreat machinery are as criminal as people who hurt animals. Anybody who hurts animals offends God, as their Creator. Anybody who mistreats machinery offends the generations of men who toiled to invent and perfect them. Which is tantamount to offending God. The great Manzoni used to say . . ."

"You and your great Manzoni can go to the devil," the old woman cut him off. He had read and reread all of Manzoni. He knew by heart the key passages of *The Betrothed*, a book whose margins he had filled with his clean, precise, beautiful handwriting. When he was a boy (the oldest of a horde of children) on a big farm in the Valley, he had gone to school on a cart pulled by a cow that spent the day grazing outside the schoolhouse. It was a kind of cow-driven cataclysm, for his brothers and sisters rode along with him; each day's journey wasn't ended until the next day. Then, the women from nearby farms would appear laden with basketsful of dead pullets and ducklings, which the mother of the horde had to replace with live specimens.

Because he had to help support this horde, he only finished grammar school; still, he had the best penmanship in the entire province. Afterward, he had read all the books he'd been able to lay hands on, until at long last he discovered Manzoni. Thereafter he read no further, having decided that Manzoni was all-encompassing. For her part, the old lady at one time had liked Manzoni well enough. However, after hearing his name once too often she had come to loathe him.

"You leave Manzoni out of it," the old man growled. "What we're talking about is an irresponsible idiot who mistreats machinery."

"He has nothing to do with it either," the old woman retorted. "Pick your fights with the sharecropper who uses the machinery. I suppose you think the boy should drop everything to wipe off your infernal machinery."

"Then he doesn't know the first thing about farming," the old man pontificated. "Farming is a serious business, not something you take on as a hobby."

They left the farmyard and made their way toward the center of the village. Once in the little square, the old man stopped reverently before a miserable, decrepit cottage behind an enormous bronze bust on a stone pedestal.

(The old man had his own sacred Trinity of personages that he revered as much as the Divine Three-in-One, and it was comprised of Manzoni, Verdi, and Napoleon. Only once in his life had the old man gone abroad, and he went straight to Paris. From the Gare de Lyon he took a taxi over to the Invalides. There he paid homage to Napoleon's tomb, hopped back in the taxi, and went straight to the station, ignoring the rest of Paris.)

A few steps from the historic cottage there was a building lit by quaint lanterns which faced a large courtyard. The old man moved over to decipher a little sign decorated with an unusual arabesque.

"Unbelievable," he exclaimed. "The idea of opening a restaurant in this flea-bitten town in the middle of nowhere. The boy is a lunatic."

"Unlike that fool who in a village half this size and twice as remote opened a huge store full of stoves, bicycles, rifles, motorcycles, Gramophones, etc. etc. Now that was true insanity, particularly in 1906."

"That was Progress," the old man said, spitting out the "P" to make sure she knew it was capitalized.

(In 1907, actually, the old man, living in a remote village in the Valley, renovated an ancient house, converting it into a vast palace with great ladies painted all around, and inside installed two agencies to rent machinery. Two businesses that had never before been seen in the provinces, with metal shutters to roll down at night over huge display windows, as if the shops were smack in the middle of the Galleria in Milan. Later the local doctor turned one of the shops into an outpatient clinic, which hardly called for windows, and the other became the squalid workshop of a poor soul who made straw stools.)

The old man refused to let the old woman keep pestering him. These were arguments he had heard time out of mind and he knew them all by heart. And besides, now his attention was riveted on the unusual arabesque that ornamented the little sign.

"It's his signature!" he howled finally. "Will you look at that! The first letter is his profile, complete with nose, mustache, eye, and forelock! What kind of nonsense is that!"

"People in glass houses," the old woman scoffed. "I take it you've never seen your own signature?"

(The old man, apart from his extraordinary calligraphy, had a signature which was a phenomenon in its own right. As he penned his name, people would stop what they were doing to watch tensely, holding their breath. First he would trace out the initials of his two given names and surname, meticulously spaced—he never varied by a millimeter—then he would finish off the given names and surname with great aplomb, closing the whole maneuver with a grand complex of flourishes and arabesques of growing intensity till at last the signature stood, a masterpiece of lacework and filligree. The entire process lived, like a finale of Verdi.)

They retraced their route and shortly found themselves back at the large white house with green shutters. It was not, after all, a house but rather a complex of buildings arranged on three sides of a rectangular courtyard. The main building revealed the personality of its creator and builder, for it looked like a compendium of second thoughts; rather than being a house with stories and wings, it was a complex of stories and wings without any proper main house.

The old man shook his head. "Poor boy," he said sadly. "He's throwing away his money on bricklayers."

"Will you shut up, you who threw away all your own money on bricklayers and then finished off mine too."

The old man's attention was drawn to the large garage; it was well built, in fact, for it even had a small but complete workshop. "Look at that," the old man cried, moving toward the worktable. "I had one exactly like it in my shop. German make. The Germans ought to be put to work doing nothing but making tools."

The cabinet above the worktable was open and inside

could be seen a quantity of machine tools, each one fastidiously hanging in its own place, a black silhouette representing the particular piece of equipment painted on the white background. "See that pressure gauge? It's mine," the old man noted. "So's that monkey wrench."

Inside the garage were sheltered a small diesel truck, two Spiders, a Fiat Millecento, three bicycles, and a Guzzino car.

"A machine fetishist, that's what he is," the old man growled.

"Look who's talking," the old woman retorted. "The only man in creation who seasoned his salad with lubricating oil. If you had any sense you'd know the boy only uses one of the cars. The rest belong to the children and the help."

"Oh yes, the help," the old man snorted. Then he analyzed the clutch of cars and pronounced sentence on them. "The four of them taken together aren't worth as much as my Scat."

They went out and wandered among the buildings. One of these had a scaffolding built against the south side. "What is he up to now?" the old man cried in alarm. "Building yet another of these airplane hangars?"

"It's the house the married son is building for himself," the old lady explained.

The old man shook his head. "Look at that balcony," he howled. "It's begging for an act of God. The son's a worse fool than his father."

"You're wrong. The son's a genius," the old woman asserted.

"He's stubborn like his mother," the old man declared. "All the children are stubborn like their mother. And their mother is more stubborn than three women put together. The first time I saw her, I had her number."

(This had happened before the War. The old man had gone off to look for "the boy" who had been working in Milan for some years. An unknown girl had let him into the house. As soon as the son came home, the old man demanded, "Who is that woman?" "My wife," his son replied placidly, and that closed the subject, for the son maintained that if his parents had taken the liberty of getting married without letting him know, it was his sacrosanct privilege to do the same. In fact, he had told his mother but made her promise to keep it between the two of them, since he was ashamed to tell his father that he was getting married. A question of modesty—but leaving modesty aside, it was now the fashion.)

They went inside the house and climbed the stairs to the second floor. The bedroom was empty and the bed was neatly made. "Still out on the town, both of them," the old man snorted. "What a family."

"She sleeps in the downstairs bedroom," the old woman explained. "They sleep apart just as we've always done."

The closet was open and the old man stuck his nose inside. "Appalling!" he cried. "Look at the silly suits he wears!"

"Nothing to compare with the suits you used to wear," the old woman spoke out. "I've never forgotten them. High noon in mid-August, and there you'd be in your blue corduroy riding pants, your black leather leggings, your black jacket, your white shirt with its starched collar, your black bowler and your tightly rolled umbrella, looking like an eccentric English financier."

"There are certain things which you've never been able to understand," the old man replied.

"What about when you used to go to town with the cat?" the old woman drove on mercilessly.

"If people can walk around with dogs on leashes, I don't see why I can't do the same with a cat," the old man said defensively.

"Then during the War, when you rode around on a bicycle without tires and as soon as you got to town the rims made such a racket on the pavement that people would rush to the window to see if you were the Allied liberation forces?" the old woman harped on.

(It was God's own truth; and this shameful phenomenon was not much cheered up by a few sprigs of daisies fastened to the handlebars in spring nor when, in answer to the question of what significance this outlandishness had, the old man would whisper confidentially that he had contrived it as an allegory of the Italy of Tomorrow.)

They went into the study. The lamps were lit there too, as they were throughout the house. Reassuring to a man of a certain age, coming home late at night, to find the windows all lit up as if somebody were waiting for him.

The old woman quickly fastened on an ashtray overflowing with cigarette butts on the desk. "After the trouble he's had," she said shaking her head, "he should quit smoking."

"Nonsense," the old man replied. "You never smoked a cigarette in your life and what's happened to you would have happened just the same."

"You might have the decency to keep your mouth shut," the old woman growled fiercely. "How can you talk that way when you were murdered by that vile disease that's the end of all smokers?"

"That's the falsest propaganda spread around by the medical profession who try to cover up their infinite ignorance any way they can," the old man snapped.

There were some typewritten sheets scattered across the desk and the old couple bent over to read them.

"Meaningless garble," the old man hemmed.

"It's marvelous," the old woman said.

"Journalism has ruined him," the old man answered.

"If he'd studied law as I suggested, he'd be sitting pretty now."

(To have a lawyer in the family, that had been her dream. The old man had a mania for notarized papers; few lawyers would have been able to outdo him in drafting an agreement or a contract or in begging an issue. The old woman had always dreamed of having somebody in the house with a bona fide law degree. As far as she was concerned, a degree was less a point of departure than an arrival, an end rather than a means. "Sitting pretty" meant to the old lady not where good luck or corruption or even brains could get you, i.e., sitting on top of a mountain of money. "Sitting pretty," according to her, was merely what the Supreme Authority of the State did to the citizen by conferring on him a well-deserved graduate degree. Also according to her, the State was God on Earth, and God was infallible.)

The old woman pointed to the Legal Code in the bookcase. "Maybe he's changed his mind and is taking up his studies again," she said hopefully. "He's a serious boy."

"It doesn't seem to me that a serious boy would be gone from his house at this hour," the old man said severely.

"Keep still, will you. You must have come home a thousand times after three A.M., singing at the top of your lungs," the old woman reproved him angrily. "Anyhow, it's only two o'clock."

Just then the church bell rang three and the notes filled the night. At the same time a Fiat shifted gears as it rounded the corner into the courtyard. Out of it bounced a man with a mustache singing *Vaya con Dios* at the top of his lungs. He left the car right in the middle of the courtyard, meandered over, and started to fool with the lock to the front door.

"He drinks white wine," the old man pronounced with the confidence of an expert. "You can tell by the sound of his voice. Red wine gives your voice a heartier timbre."

Meanwhile the man had worked his way in and, still singing, was marching up the squeaky oak staircase.

"He has worries," the old man added, even more expertly than before. "This you can tell from his voice also. You never understood him, though . . ."

"We must go!" the old woman said nervously. "He mustn't find us here. He shouldn't see us!"

"And how would he be able to see us?" the old man laughed.

"We mustn't see *him*, then," the old woman insisted. "The eyes of the dead shouldn't look into the eyes of the living. Death is a disease that transmits germs even through a glance."

"Well, then I'm damned if I know what we came here for," the old man grumbled.

The man with the mustache had begun to climb a steep ladder that led through a trap door into his tiny lair.

"And he sings!" the old man exclaimed. "He sings too!"

"Yes," the old woman had to admit. "But he sings so much better than you did."

The old couple drifted into the night through the glass door on the balcony and returned to their distant graves to go on with their eternal quarreling. Meanwhile I, singing away, threw myself on the bed, my head full of confusion and my heart full of remorse.

Do You Remember, Margherita?

The Pullover

A few centuries ago, when, by fortunate accident, I began to find myself meeting Margherita every night, I was in the habit of wearing the multicolored plaid shirts I wear still today and which have the delicate feel of a horseblanket.

Margherita said to me one night: "Look Giovanni, your shirts are marvelous but I'd love to see you just once wear a nice sport sweater."

At that point I was making 290 lire a month gross—a respectable salary but it didn't leave room for arrant whims such as a pure wool sport sweater. I told Margherita so but she answered: "Don't give it a thought. I have reason to believe that somebody might make you one and give it to you. I can't tell you any more because it's a secret."

Quite a lot of time passed but, given the fact that you shouldn't look gift horses in the mouth, particularly when there patently is no gift horse, I never spoke of this "sport sweater." Margherita was the one who raised the subject again, when for some reason that escapes me, we found ourselves in Milan, legally married.

"I would have loved to see you in front of the altar with your nice dark-green sweater on. But it just wasn't possible. Since there shouldn't be secrets between husbands and wives, I'm going to tell you the truth. The person I spoke of who was going to knit the sweater was me."

The revelation touched me. "Margherita, forget about the sweater. It's the thought that counts, and besides, the radiators at the publishing house are boiling hot and I couldn't even wear it."

We didn't speak of it again. In 1938 the sky over Europe turned black. It seemed as if war was going to break out any minute and the Army said: "It is urgently necessary to recall to duty Artillery Lieutenant Guareschi, Giovanni, and send him to guard the French border." I was sent to the Piedmont and stationed in a little village called Sambuco, and my orders were to install a battery of 149 shodas (war booty from 1915–1918) and to construct atop a certain hilly rise, with wood we were to find on the spot, a sturdy redoubt, which, carefully camouflaged, was to serve as a conning tower. The men assigned to me constructed it according to my directions, and the result was both solid and of martial beauty.

Then it began to rain and one morning my aide informed me: "The conning tower is here, sir."

"What conning tower? Where?"

"Here in the valley. Our conning tower. The rain has caused it to slip down, intact."

Without the conning tower, our emplacement was like a

blind man who shoots if he is poked. Fortunately, the same day an order arrived to remove the emplacement to Argentera, further ahead, and to cover all the equipment immediately with a wooden hangar that looked like an enormous, inverted barge chopped in half lengthwise. By a chance unique in the history of the Italian army it happened that, at the same moment as the order, the materiel for the construction of these half-barges arrived. Thus it was that we moved the line ahead and covered the ammunition and artillery.

It was no easy job but in time we managed to finish it up. In fact, three days later, five important events occurred simultaneously: 1) the snow began; 2) an order arrived to put our winter wool uniforms away and begin wearing summer fatigues; 3) an order arrived to remove previously issued grenades from our kits and replace them with others not intended for target practice; 4) the latter arrived; and 5) I'm not going to tell you yet because war stories require a certain degree of suspense.

I was young and efficient and went straight to the forest where my company's tents were pitched. I found the camp already inundated in snow but, under orders, I pitilessly ordered the men in a thundering voice to remove their winter uniforms and remain at attention in their underwear until the summer fatigues arrived from Vinadio. Since already a month before I had ordered my men to billet themselves in the cabins and huts of the village, none of them was there to answer me and I shouted that I would have to take severe disciplinary measures. Later, once the men were gathered together, I went through the blizzard with them to switch the ammunition. This was a bit of a chore but one from which I returned victorious and soaked through from head to foot.

Inside the shack that I had chosen for a home I found two wonderful surprises: the stove was fired up red-hot because inside it pieces of fir wood from my glorious conning tower, chopped up providentially by my aide, were burning merrily away; and in front of the stove, there was Margherita.

Seeing me soaked to the skin, she said: "I imagined things would be like this." Then out of her suitcase she dragged a thick wad of skeins of dark-green wool and announced: "It's clear the country needs me. I'm not leaving here until I finish this sweater!"

I was just a crude soldier but I was touched. Who ever would have dared to tempt the integrity of a country that has women as heroic as Margherita?

"Margherita!" I shouted with the voice of a colonel. "This won't do at all!"

Margherita began to work with divine fury on the sweater, but it happened that a few days later the Army, reassured of the solidarity of the cordon of defense that I had created, sent me home, and so it was that the sweater and my gray-green uniform went to sleep in mothballs.

But then the storm broke and when things began to get tough for us in 1942 the Army politely requested my assistance again. I set out with great vigor to reorganize the Army but this didn't last very long because the Army fell apart in 1943 and I was sent to a German prison camp.

I came home in September 1945 and almost immediately found myself up to my eyes in the furious political struggle. I was hot under the collar even without the sweater, about which nothing more was said. But on the 17th of April, on the eve of the historic elections of 1948, I came home to find Margherita intently knitting at the dark-green sweater. "Giovanni," she explained, "the Communists are bound to win and they'll send you to Siberia, where this sweater will keep you nice and snug."

But the Communists did not win and the sweater went back into mothballs.

Thus we arrived at 1961: the children were grown up and Albertino, a second lieutenant in the Alpine Artillery, was doing his stint up in the Alto Adige. Margherita immediately took up working like a dervish on the dark-green sweater, but in the summer of 1962 I became seriously ill and the sweater disappeared again. It stayed nestled in the mothballs for a while but popped up again when our ex-Passionaria's son was born.

"This time," Margherita said with fierce determination, "I will finish it in time for Michelone to wear it when he goes into the service."

"But there are more and more conscientious objectors every day," I said. "I don't believe that the draft will exist in twenty years."

"That makes no difference," Margherita answered. "Then in twenty years I'll give it to him to celebrate his coming of age."

"The trouble is, Margherita, in a few years they're going to move the voting age down to eighteen."

"Well, in that case I'd better get a move on!" she exclaimed anxiously, starting to knit like a maniac. Then a tender look came over her face and she said in a distant voice, "Just think, Giovanni, how quickly time flies! It's been thirty-five years in the making, this silly dark-green sweater. Imagine what it would say if it could talk!"

"Probably it would say: 'Once I was a dark-green sweater, but today I'm a yellowish sweater.' "

"Tout passe, tout casse, tout lasse!" Margherita sighed.

It was a magical autumn day and some golden leaves drifted slowly and prettily past the window.

The Wedding

I informed Margherita that I had to go to town to buy a few tools and things and Jo informed me that this pleased her very much. "I'm coming too," exclaimed the domestic assistant which Divine Providence has seen fit to saddle us with. "When are you leaving?"

"Right now."

"But aren't you getting dressed?"

This worried me: for a while now my memory has been sighing wearily and going on strike and so from time to time I perform little mental aberrancies that deserve to be encapsulated in vignette form. But quickly giving myself the once-over, I relaxed.

"What do you mean, get dressed?" I answered. "Do you mean to tell me I'm not dressed?"

"Let's say you're covered with various colored rags," said Jo. "But you're not wearing what's commonly known as a 'suit.' "

"I'm not going to town to enter a beauty contest, you know," I offered. "The only reason I'm going to town is to buy a length of chain, some hinges, locks, bolts, and that sort of thing."

"Yes, but you're coming with me, and people might think you're my father and decide that I was the daughter of a tramp. I have my self-respect and therefore I feel that you should dress like a normal human being."

"Jo, it's no use your carrying on like this," Margherita said in the anguished tone used by unhappy women who are content to suffer in silence. "Bear in mind that I wasn't able to persuade him to dress properly even for his own wedding." (If they weren't able to talk as a consolation, how could unhappy women content to suffer in silence manage to survive?)

Jo glared at me, horrified. "In other words, he had the nerve to get married decked out like this?"

"More or less," I explained. "In any case you couldn't see it because I was wearing a checkered coat."

"Are you saying that you got married wearing an *overcoat?*"

"Sure. It was monstrous cold and the inside of the church was like a refrigerator."

Jo shook her head, tittering. "Mrs. Guareschi," she said, "I'd love to see your album of wedding pictures!"

"Album of wedding pictures?" Margherita laughed bitterly. "We arrived at the church in one taxi followed by a taxi containing the four witnesses. Naturally the usual photographer was camped out in the square waiting for business. He took one look, made a face, and turned his back on us. According to him, we weren't even worth considering as customers."

"Then in fact you don't have anything at all to remember your wedding by!" Jo exclaimed horrified.

"I've got him," Margherita said, pointing at me.

The event in question happened approximately thirty years ago. Then, Italy was a predominantly agricultural nation and dirt poor, while today it is a predominantly industrial nation and rich as Croesus.

We got married in February and the marriage cost me one eagle (an eagle being five silver lire) and I had to insist on the parish priest's taking my eagle. It was a modest offering, to be sure, but it was the right thing to do because the marriage, which has turned into one of the most solid of this century, simply wasn't worth more than five lire.

The sacred rite, if you could call it that, happened in Milan at the church of Santa Francesca Romana, just following a very sumptuous society wedding. The church was still full of flowers, the altar sparkling with candles, and a rich red carpet was extended from the altar to the door. Just as we were coming in, we heard a shout and a cloud of altar boys was let loose inside the church. Working like locusts, one group devoured the flowers, another removed the silver-plated busts of various episcopal eminences from the altar, and still another group, inch by inch as Margherita and I walked up the aisle followed by our four witnesses, rolled up the rich red carpet before we got a chance to set our unsanitary feet on it. It was a lightning quick ceremony propelled by the priest's peremptory commands: "All rise! Now kneel! Now sit! Now kneel! Say *I do!* The ring!"—and so on. I remember that afterward, the organist was still waiting up in the organ loft and as we started to leave he began to play the Lohengrin march, but a shriek from the officiating priest stopped him cold.

To be sure, a film of that wedding would be worth its weight in platinum.

Jo listened to the story and then said to Margherita, "I suppose as a young girl you dreamed of a wedding with banks of flowers and candles and music . . ."

Margherita shrugged her shoulders. "Jo, in those days, Italy was a poor country and for us girls it was enough if the future husband turned up at the wedding ceremony. In those days, our electrical appliances amounted to a clothes iron, and often instead of being electric it ran by gas."

"What misery," Jo sighed. "You certainly got along on precious little. What were you wearing?"

"A skirt and sweater, I think," Margherita said. "In any case you couldn't see it because I was wearing an overcoat. It was a beautiful overcoat."

"It certainly was!" I exclaimed. "The officers in the Royal Army didn't wear the same uniforms all the time like the officers in the Republican Army, whether they were out on bivouac or stationed in town. Since I was an artillery officer, I had a fabulous blue cloak. When I finished my first tour of duty I had it dyed black and she made a marvelous wedding coat out of it. And people still talk about that wedding even today."

The Bicycle

Jo, the domestic assistant that Fate has deposited on the rubble of our humble home, had an outburst of rebellion. "Can't we have a moment's peace here?" she exclaimed, interrupting her reading of her favorite weekly. "We've worked like demons to fix up Sophia, Lollo, Sandra Milo, Vittorio Gassman, Claudia Cardinale; after a bitter struggle we've managed to marry off the adorable Countess Gallarate; we've sweated blood to straighten out Iva Zanicchi's domestic plight, and now that we might be able to enjoy a well-deserved vacation, here we have Rita Pavone cropping up again. Will somebody please tell me why even this unfortunate father has to find something to say about his daughter's wedding?"

"He's an old-fashioned man," Margherita said. "He thinks it's abnormal for his daughter to marry a man who already has a wife."

"Nonsense!" the girl retorted. "What business is it of his if Rita's fiancé's wife has announced to the newspapers that she's perfectly delighted that they're getting married, Rita and her husband? And besides, excuse me for bringing it up, if one man can marry another man in Rotterdam and the newspapers print the wedding picture as if it happened every day, why stamp your feet over a perfectly normal marriage between a man and a woman?"

"Jo," I said, "why are you interested in any of these things?"

"And what things should I be interested in, according to you?" our domestic assistant demanded.

"Jo," I answered calmly, "there are a lot of things much more important than the petty affairs of movie stars. I mean things that involve the spiritual and material welfare of the whole world and which are truly worth talking about and even getting mad about. What possible importance can it have, Jo, if a nightclub singer marries Henri or Alistair or Gunther? Or if some TV starlet has a child and never bothers to get married? In my day . . ."

"I get it!" Jo interrupted me aggressively. "In your day, what you're always saying, people were serious and were interested only in science, literature, painting, poetry, philosophy, history, photography, mathematics, chemistry, archaeology, and things of that nature."

"Not by the wildest stretch of the imagination," I protested. "I only wanted to say that in my day, scandals didn't exist, there weren't any of these noisy lawsuits, divorces, separations, love affairs, suicides . . ."

Jo started to laugh. "The Garden of Eden!" she hooted. "No woman cheated on her husband, no man fell in love with his wife's best friend, nobody got divorces, nobody killed himself."

"Just so," I said. "Of course people accidentally fell out of windows, or accidentally left open the gas-cock, or after accidentally killing their wife and a family friend by inadvertently allowing two bullets to escape from the gun they were cleaning, when they ran to fetch the doctor, they tripped on the stairs and accidentally let loose still another bullet which passed clean through their own heart, purely by chance. The Age of Unfortunate Accidents. I was a reporter at the time and can vouch that your scandal-sheet, yellow journalism was strictly relegated to a single thirty-two line column."

"Thirty-two?" Jo said amazed. "Why thirty-two, precisely?"

"After all these years, do you know I never have been able to find out. Even then there were divorces, scandals, movie stars' escapades, cases of adultery, obstreperous brutalities, and suicides; but they could only happen in America. The same thing went for people who wrote stories and novels—if you were going to talk about adultery, you had to set your story in America. And, for example, these gypsy Rock festivals would have been unthinkable then. All the touring hippies would have been arrested before they'd traveled a hundred yards."

"Why in the world?"

"Because at that point the people in charge had announced that the Italian people had become intelligent, talented, serious, dignified, and opposed to frivolities. Everybody pretended to believe it, but actually not a single soul did."

Jo was amazed. "How did the journalists manage to fill up the pages of the newspapers and magazines?"

"The newspapers and magazines," I explained, "were few and far between and even the ones we had were stunted in comparison with today's. A single weekly today has more pages than all the weeklys then put together. Still it was hard work, being a journalist in those days, because in spite of everything the city page had to be filled up somehow. I made the rounds every day, first to the police barracks, then to the jail, then to the emergency entrance of the hospital—

with the result that I discovered such exciting items as 'Farmer's Wife Slices Off Finger Peeling Potatoes,' 'Cyclist Falls, Suffers Concussion,' or 'Chicken Thief Captured.' Things to really sit down and cry about. So finally one sunny day I gave up with the fingerless farmer's wives, fallen bicyclists, and chicken thieves of the world, and began to invent news items. Naturally they were much more entertaining than real facts. They were even more true-to-life. Besides, it gave me a lot of time to run after girls."

Jo exploded with laughter. "Do you mean to tell me you ran after girls?" she said howling.

"Yes," I said. "But it wasn't much work because I always went around on a bicycle."

"With that mustache?" she tittered.

"No," Margherita put in. "He didn't have it then. He let it grow in the concentration camp to have something to chew on when he was so hungry his knees were weak."

"I can't imagine him without a mustache," Jo said.

"I can," Margherita said. "He was young, handsome, and always wore plus-fours."

"Knickers, if you please," I corrected her. "They gave a young man a decidedly sporty look. Anyhow, for a bicycle they were a lot more practical than using clothespins to keep long pants up away from the gearchain."

Jo was going out of her mind with glee. "So he went riding around after girls on a bicycle," she bubbled madly. "Did he ever catch any, I wonder?"

"I should say I did," I answered. "Now if a fellow doesn't have an Alfa Romeo Sprint, he hasn't got a prayer. But then the girls didn't have any trouble accepting a ride on a bicycle and sat like Amazons on the crossbar. Particularly at night, you understand."

"The good old days," Jo laughed.

"The good old seats," Margherita corrected her. "He also had an oil lamp for a headlight and if his conquests weren't careful they wound up with a black face."

Jo shook her head. "Poor girls. They certainly let themselves be treated like bundles in those days."

"Not all of them," Margherita said. "I know one girl who, one night, gave him the ultimatum: either get rid of the oil lamp and buy a nice electric light, or I'll drop you."

"So what did he do?" Jo said.

"Well, it involved an insane expense," I answered. "And besides, I'm not the type who lets himself be ruined by women. Rather than change headlights, I said, I'll change girlfriends."

"Well, I hope she gave him the high sign!" Jo said indignantly.

"No," I explained. "She sighed and answered back, 'Love is sacrifice. I'll put up with the oil headlight.' "

"What an idiot," Jo said. "I was dating a fruitcake who went on wearing flappy pants with cuffs after I told him I liked tapered pants with no cuffs. I dropped him flat."

"I did the opposite. I preferred to marry the fellow with the oil headlamp."

"You're more vindictive than I am," Jo decided.

The Ultimatum

"This time nobody's going to stop me," Margherita informed me. "I'm going straight to the union."

"Even you, a union?" I said, amazed. "Which one is it?"

"The same one as Jo's," Margherita answered.

"But you're an employer," Jo protested. "You're not a worker."

"And I suppose what I did for more than twenty years, before I had help in the house, I suppose that wasn't work?" Margherita retorted.

She spread out before my eyes a newspaper where it was clearly written that according to the calculations of the experts, a housewife should, if she were to be reimbursed for her time according to the existing laws, taking into account a normal working day plus overtime, earn approximately 450,000 lire monthly.

"Therefore," Margherita concluded happily, "twenty years equals 240 months times 400,000 (you see I'm deducting for breakage, holidays, and withholding tax) equals 96,000,000 lire you owe me."

I objected, saying the figure arrived at was ridiculous, given that she should have computed in the gradual devaluation of the lira from 1936 to 1956. Furthermore, she had to subtract the various payments received in money and in kind over the years.

"You go on and compute and calculate all you like," Margherita exclaimed. "You'll never be able to deny that I have served as a domestic in your house for at least 240 months, work that is worth 450,000 lire per month under the current labor statutes."

"I'm being careful not to deny it, Margherita. In fact I'm happy to recognize your rights because it only confirms what I've been saying for a long time: a woman very often earns more working at home as a domestic servant than she could possibly working away from home."

Jo bristled like a cat. "Here we go again with the usual story of the woman who should stay at home to knit socks and make pleasant conversation."

"Not at all, Jo," I answered. "That would be like saying that women like Grazia Deledda would do better writing only grocery lists or that women like Madame Curie would do better studying recipes for beef Stroganoff than the phenomena of physics and chemistry. There are women with brains far more efficient than those of men, women better cut out for certain jobs and professions than men are; it would be a great disaster for mankind if these women were not able to exercise the activities for which they are particularly well suited. I only frown on the fact that today the practice of women, regardless of who they are, is to abandon their families to work away from home even when there's no real need for them to do so."

Jo started to laugh, shaking her head. "And as for the dignity of womankind, where does that leave us? When a woman no longer has to depend on her husband for a living because she knows how to make one for herself, she can consider herself on an equal footing with him."

"This is absolutely true," Margherita agreed.

"No it's not, because even if the wife works away from

home the husband will never agree to cook, wash dishes, mend clothes, do ironing, go shopping, or launder the linen. And above all, he would never agree to bear children. Whatever she does for a living, women will always be on an unequal footing with men."

Jo pointed an accusing finger at me. "So according to you, women are inferior to men!"

"I didn't say anything about inferiority. I just said unequal. In Russia and China, where they have achieved total equality of rights, women work as streetcleaners, firemen, hod carriers, bricklayers, soldiers, miners—exactly like men. But it's the woman who goes on bringing children into the world. Equality of rights between men and women will exist only when they have not only maternity wards but also paternity wards in hospitals."

Jo looked at Margherita disgustedly. "Have you ever noticed how when he doesn't have anything intelligent to say he makes everything into a joke?"

"It's not true, Jo," I said defensively. "Humor walks the path of the paradox, and the path of the paradox, as a very clever and important man once said, is the shortcut to truth. There's nothing to laugh at—equality of rights exists only when there is equality of duties. And the crux is this: men try to impose on women a false equality of duties—false, I repeat, because no one in the world will ever be able to impose on any man the duty of bringing children into the world and nursing them."

"Here we are again with the joke about children," Jo laughed.

"Children are no joke," I answered. "And neither is it a joke that too often this highly touted prosperity, invented by men, comes to be paid for by women. Too often the woman is the victim of Progress which, artificially creating new needs, new indispensables, makes a family spend more and more. A problem which too often is solved by husbands sending their wives off to work in a factory or in an office. There are an awful lot of masculine brains working feverishly to the detriment of womankind. And if once upon a time, art, poetry, literature exalted women for being mothers, lovers, muses, heroines, angels or devils, now women are only praised for being workers."

"It seems to me that's only fair," Margherita observed. "Women work too and it's only fair that they're given credit for it."

"Right," I said, "if it weren't a case of demagogy and publicity. The importance of women is the determining factor for most industrial and commerical campaigns—if a film, a record, a novel, a household product doesn't please women, it won't sell. Therefore, 99 per cent of all publicity is aimed at women. They don't leave you alone for a moment: they hammer away at you incessantly, they persecute you. They compel you to buy entertaining gadgets, interesting but not necessary, they seduce you with smiles, praises, gifts, contests with prizes. By exalting the importance of woman socially and politically, at the same time they convince her to give herself a nice home permanent, to paint her eyes, to soften her hands and skin with lotions and creams. And to pay for this the poor women must look for work away from home."

"But it seems only just," Jo asserted. "How else can one have a TV, a record player, a washing machine, a refrigerator, a freezer, a dishwasher, a rotisserie, a vacuum cleaner, the proper cosmetics, some clothes to wear when you face the world, a weekend trip, a month at the sea, and so forth, if the woman doesn't help her husband?"

"Just what I was saying," I answered. "It's women who pay for Prosperity, a consumer product invented by men."

"If there's equality of rights, there's also equality of duties," the girl maintained. "And it's only just that everybody pays his or her share."

"Very just," I admitted. "It's too bad that ultimately it's the family that suffers, that's in a state of crisis today, above all because the woman can't take care of her family since she's so occupied with her work away from home. The result being, in countries where women have been most successful in becoming important and self-sufficient the family unit is in an advanced state of decrepitude, and juvenile delinquency and the dissatisfaction of women are most acute. And at the same time, even though men haven't yet given birth to babies in those countries, they help women in every way possible: they wash dishes, they sweep the floors, they cook, they buy groceries—things that here would be humiliating to any self-respecting man even if he does take the car and go off alone on weekends while the wife slaves away in a factory or an office."

Jo didn't agree. "Your little speech," she said, "is the kind an embittered and jealous man would make who had had a childhood more difficult than that of kids today."

"I don't think so," I answered. "My first automobile I bought at least twenty-nine years ago."

Jo did a quick bit of arithmetic and gave a triumphant shout. "There you are! Your first car at the age of twenty-eight, when you were already a doddering old man!"

"Not exactly doddering, I wouldn't say," Margherita put in. "In those days we got old more slowly than today." Then she turned to me with a determined squint in her eye. "Giovanni, you owe me 96,000,000 lire!"

"Okay," I said. "Let's make it an even hundred and not talk about it any more."

We never talked about it again.

Bluebeard

"I need to go home for a few days, to breathe my own air, to seek out the thoughts of my childhood," Jo said abruptly one day.

"Have a good trip," Margherita said. "When are you leaving?"

"When I'm sure that you can do without me."

"I ran this house by myself for so many years and I don't think . . ." Margherita tried to object. But the girl interrupted her.

"You're thinking of the days when the only machine in your house was a corkscrew. An elementary machine, absolutely ridiculous when you consider its perfect simplicity of design and intent; however, to this day it is a machine which you are not capable of using because you haven't grasped the fact that the corkscrew must penetrate the cork directly in the center, otherwise when you pull in a vertical direction either the cork or the neck of the bottle will break. Or the corkscrew itself."

This was true in the strictest possible sense and Margherita, who was allergic to machines of every size and shape, went into a pout.

"Let us begin our lessons with the washing machine," Jo decreed. "And the first thing we must learn about the washing machine is that it is the machine situated where laundry and ironing are done, that is, in the storeroom, while the machine situated in the kitchen is the dishwasher."

"This I could have figured out for myself," Margherita protested.

"After what happened the time you put the dishes in the washing machine, I should hope so," Jo answered with patent sarcasm.

We went into the washing and ironing area, which however often it is called a "storeroom," giving the impression that it is small, still happens to be the largest room in our house. Jo introduced Margherita to the washing machine, identifying its brand, model, and salient characteristics.

"It's very easy to operate," she explained. "You raise the lid, you fill it with cold or pre-heated water all the way up to this line. Then you drop a cupful of detergent into the water (just the detergent, not the cup, please), you slosh the detergent around, you put in the laundry (white things with white things), no more than four kilos at a time, then you turn this button to select a temperature . . ."

"I'm not turning anything!" Margherita said firmly.

"But if you don't select a temperature and a length of time for washing, the machine won't work," the girl cried.

"*He'll* select them," Margherita said.

He is me, and I nodded calmly, since for many years I've known how to run the machines in my house. But the girl—

probably because it's Margherita I married and not her—
would not accept the compromise Margherita had proposed.

"Him! Him! It's always *him!*" she shrieked. "It's as if
when *he* isn't around the whole world comes screeching to a
halt. If *he* isn't around you walk, because you've never
bothered to learn how to drive a car. If a fuse blows and *he*
isn't around you stand in the dark because you're terrified of
going near the fusebox."

"I don't stand in the dark!" Margherita protested indignantly. "I'm perfectly capable of lighting a candle."

"And if the electricity goes off and the furnace goes out?"

"I light a fire in the fireplace."

"And if the pump fails to bring water up out of the well?"

"I can take the cap off a bottle of mineral water," Margherita said.

Jo was appalled. "Mrs. Guareschi," she cried in exasperation, "you haven't caught on to the fact that we're living in
the 1960s and that women run businesses, make important
scientific discoveries, steer ships across oceans, and orbit the
earth in space capsules. And they do all this without any
help from *him*. Hasn't anybody told you that women have
equal rights now, self-sufficiency and independence?"

"Certainly I'm aware of it," Margherita said. "Even I
read the newspapers."

"If so, don't you then realize that if you put yourself in
the position of always needing *him,* you give up your self-
sufficiency, your independence, in effect your dignity?"

Margherita's powers of reasoning are pseudological—she
is unaware of the true nature of things and is content to
skim off the cream.

"It's not clear to me," Margherita exclaimed, "why I give

up my dignity if, instead of working the washing machine myself, I make *him* work it."

Jo, who is of the school of the Italian Christian Workers' Association, has a mind as open as the times. She began to laugh. "Mrs. Guareschi, you don't seem to understand that if you give the man charge of the buttons, he becomes the absolute dictator of the house."

Stupidly, I started to snicker and Jo looked at me sternly. "Naturally *he* would find it amusing, being the absolute dictator of the house."

"Not at all. It's the part about giving the man charge of the buttons that I think is so funny. Because if one falls off I sew it back on."

Jo eyed Margherita severely and she was forced to admit it. "I let him do it, you know, because he's so good at these things. When he sews a button on with a little copper thread, there's nothing in the world that can get it off again."

Jo gave up and decided to cut the lesson short. "All right. We'll skip the electrical appliances. *He* will deal with them. Let us go on to things which have nothing to do with electricity and machines. Since you will have to straighten out the bedrooms, keep in mind that *he* has special ideas about how *he* likes his bed made."

"This I know perfectly well," Margherita exclaimed. "Nobody's ever managed to please him."

"I have!" Jo protested. "It doesn't take an Einstein to figure out that when you make a bed for *him,* you have to tuck sheets and blankets in securely at the foot of the bed, otherwise as soon as *he* crawls in and pulls the covers over his head, his feet appear at the other end."

"I know this perfectly well," Margherita exclaimed.

"When his feet come out at the other end he gets mean as a badger and you can hear him through closed doors way at the other end of the house. I remember when we were living in Milan, where it was bitter cold because we didn't have central heating, he set up an ingenious solution. He bought two wood poles as long as the mattress, and with four finger-length bolts he trapped the sheet and the covers between the two poles down at the foot of the bed so that, once you put the poles under the mattress, the unit of bedcovers became immobile. Naturally I made buttonholes at the bottom of the sheets and blankets in order to let the points of the bolts pass through without making unsightly holes."

Jo eyed me with faint disgust. "Now I understand those holes I discovered in the old linen. How vile, particularly from the point of view of hygiene."

"Not at all," Margherita explained. "At the end of each pole he tied a long cord that was threaded through a little pulley attached to the ceiling. The two pulleys on the ceiling ran on little brass rails. These little brass rails (garden-variety curtain tracks, you know the kind), thanks to a wooden bracket braced against the lintel of the balcony door, ran from the ceiling above the bed to the balcony over the courtyard. When we got up in the morning, he pulled the two cords, the unit of bedcovers came away from the mattress, rose up to the ceiling, and as soon as he opened the jalousie doors (which didn't jam against the little brass rails because he made little corresponding notches in them) the whole business chugged off to the balcony, where he tied the other end down to the balcony rail, and it was simple as pie to give the sheets and blankets a good beating."

Jo winced.

"It was a beautiful thing, believe me," Margherita went on. "All apart from the spectacular aspect of it, which brought hordes of people to the courtyard. The whole enterprise had something naval about it, something very Mediterranean."

Margherita turned toward me. "Do you remember, Giovanni, that accountant who lived across the way who would yell every morning, 'The destiny of Italy is on the Sea!' "

"Yes, and I remember the other things he inevitably yelled: 'Hoist the jib! Lower the mizzen! Hard astarboard! Spanish galleon ahoy!' "

Jo considered all this calmly and then said to Margherita, "Well, I understand everything except one thing. How did you manage to get along without *him* when *he* was in the concentration camp and in prison?"

Margherita shrugged. "When *he's* not around, then I remember that women now have equal rights."

"Okay," Jo said. "I'll take a holiday this summer. But I'm not very happy about the idea of his going back to playing Bluebeard again."

"Graybeard," Margherita corrected, with subtle malice.

Passionaria Deserts Us

✳

A poor writer goes out of his mind trying to create a few characters to use in his stories and what happens the minute he has the characters where he wants them? One by one they abandon him. I've managed to come up with six: Don Camillo and Peppone for the "outside" stories, for export; Albertino, Passionaria, Margherita and Hamlet the dog for the "inside" stories, about the family.

Hamlet was the first to leave me—in the usual trite way, ending his days under the wheels of a car. The second to go was Albertino, in an ever triter way, by becoming a paterfamilias. Now even Passionaria's left my little world, moving from the literary to the lactary realm.

You'll no doubt tell me it's my own fault for not stopping their growth at a certain point in time and keeping them tidily at the ages of eight and ten. And in the same fashion Margherita would have remained young always. Actually it wouldn't have been difficult to do, because an author's characters are only puppets and his to do with as he pleases —but it's hard, if not impossible, to keep the puppeteer from growing old.

Thus my characters have grown older along with me and there's nobody left except Don Camillo and Peppone, who, having been immortalized in the movies, still keep on trying to be themselves. But it's a real chore, given the fact that the situation has changed considerably since 1946, and in order to accomplish anything at all they have to emigrate and work abroad. Hence we have Don Camillo in Russia, disguised as a Comrade. Maybe tomorrow they will go to America, with Peppone disguised as a priest.

To get back to the "inside" story, let me say that a few days ago when I found myself rather unexpectedly standing beside Passionaria, all dressed in white, I didn't get overly emotional. Even when we started into the church I kept calm, because I remembered a day long ago when I first brought Passionaria to school—my October Revolution.

The reason I remembered it was because I was thinking of the time when Passionaria left my life to fly into the arms of the Government. She was to become a brick in a wall comprised of millions of bricks, and this necessary tyranny filled my heart with bitterness. The squadrons had assembled. Mammas and pappas had withdrawn to the middle of the town square, and their babies were left all alone, up against the schoolhouse wall. The only child missing from the group was Passionaria, and I started to let go her fingers. At that moment the school doors opened and the children began to file in.

There was a taxi waiting at the corner. I headed for it on the run, threw open the door, and hurled myself in like a sack of potatoes. The car sped off through the streets of Milan and headed toward the outskirts. And when the car pulled up in front of the seaplane station on the lake we got out.

I say "we" because Passionaria was with me. She had gone along with the Revolution.

The paths around the lake were full of sunlight and secluded places and we had a marvelous time. But all the time I was thinking that at home the Government would be waiting for us: Margherita. This spoiled the fun a little. But when we returned home around noon Margherita asked Passionaria how it had gone, and Passionaria answered that it had gone just fine, the teacher lady was nice, etc. etc. Then she looked at me and winked, because we had plotted beforehand precisely what she would say. So, with a wink of an eye, my October Revolution was finished.

It was, if I'm not mistaken, October 1949. This is what I was thinking of when I marched into the church with Passionaria on my arm, down toward the altar covered with many-colored flowers of the field and young heads of wheat. So my old heart was still full of hope.

For that reason I didn't get excited when I saw the young girl kneeling in front of the altar next to that fellow whose name figured on the marriage license next to Passionaria's. It didn't even worry me when the priest asked the fellow if it suited him to take Passionaria as his lawful wedded wife and the fellow didn't bat an eye before saying yes. Naturally it suited him to marry her. Any man in his right mind would have said yes. And when the priest asked Passionaria if she would take the fellow to be her lawful wedded husband, I couldn't help smiling nastily. Now, I thought, comes the great moment when she says, "Never! I want to stay with

my pappa!" Then she stands up, we go out together, jump
in the car that's waiting outside, and we take a merry ride
along the banks of the Po, enjoying ourselves as much as
that famous first day of school in 1949.

Instead she answers yes. In an undertone, so as not to
upset me, because I was right there, all of two steps behind
her. Still, she answered yes. Undoubtedly the pressure of the
situation; it was the first time she had been involved in
anything like it.

Margherita, who was standing beside me, sighed. "It happened to me the same way. You never think clearly at times
like this."

I had faith in the good sense of the priest, who was then
still a friend of mine. "Now watch," I said to Margherita.
"Father Rossi will say to her, 'Hold on! Think it over, don't
be so hasty. Let's talk about it again in three or four years.'"
Instead the treacherous priest, whom I shall never speak to
again, took her at her word and peremptorily announced
that the two children were man and wife.

Margherita looked at me, perplexed. "It's not the last
word yet," I hissed. "You'll see: either she or the witnesses
will refuse to sign the register." Instead they all signed, even
Minardi and Piren whom I'd chosen as witnesses thinking
them faithful and loyal friends.

But it wasn't over yet. I still had two aces up my sleeve:
Fernandel and Gino Cervi. I had ordained Fernandel a
priest. I had given him a parish with a little bit of life in it. I
promoted him to monsignor. As for Cervi, I elected him
mayor of Fernandel's parish. I begged them to intervene,
but the two of them abandoned me mercilessly. Don Camillo

because, he said, he was in mufti. Peppone because he'd forgotten his mayor's mustache.

"Intervene as Maigret," I said to him. "Arrest the priest. Arrest him for being the prime culprit behind that new monument to Verdi that you saw out there in the square." He answered that as Maigret he was out of his territory and didn't want to get in hot water with either the Sûreté or with Simenon.

"Now what?" Margherita said, very worried. "Isn't there anything we can do at all?"

I told her not to get excited and when the wedding dinner was over, Passionaria and her would-be husband got into the car to go on their honeymoon. I followed them in my Spider. Right behind me was a line of cars—all the wedding guests.

When we got to the Via Emilia we all stopped for the farewell toast and at that moment I took Passionaria aside and gave her a piece of my mind. She answered that now she was married and she had to go where her husband went.

"It's against the law to desert the conjugal abode," I informed her. "But there's no law that says you can't desert the conjugal car and come home with your father." She explained to me that in fact legally you would have to consider the conjugal car a part of the conjugal abode. Even more so, since it was a hardtop sedan and not a convertible. So I came back alone.

"Margherita," I said to the pale lady who was waiting anxiously at the gate of our deserted house, "I'm beginning to suspect that our daughter is irreparably married."

That night for various reasons I couldn't sleep and Hamlet bayed long and mournfully. But Margherita and I were the only ones who could hear him, because Hamlet is buried under the first Christmas tree in the left row, a hearty fir tree which has grown fairly large in the last fifteen years.

It's a sad lot for a writer who is left with only one of his six characters. And, what's worse, a practically unusable character, since Margherita is already a grandmother, and you can't make jokes about grandmothers.

Was I Beautiful
in My Wool Skirt!

☆

"Who's this ugly girl with the big round eyes who looks just like Michelone (son of the ex-Passionaria)?" Jo asked, pointing to a photograph in a family album she was leafing through. For a while now Jo had diligently been studying the cherished images of my past that fill up our family albums. The first time I discovered this activity of hers, it irritated me, but it didn't bother Jo. "It's my right to know what kind of house I'm working in," she explained. "I know nothing about your past."

"And what business is it of yours? I've never investigated *yours*."

"A fine time you'd have," she said, "since I don't have a past."

"Long or short, everybody has some kind of past."

"Today's young people don't," she said. "And never will have. Think of youth as a trip, a trip for its own sake, going where you want to and stopping where you please and with whom you please; it's sort of like a group tour where everything would be programed except that you don't bother going where the tour director says you have to go, you simply *get off*. Kids today all have more or less the same pulse, the same life tone, the same tastes, the same entertainments, the same goals, the same experience. The past only has value if it's a personal thing, not something collective. That's why I say I don't have a past."

"Okay," I said. "But since I have one and it's strictly personal, I don't see why you're so interested in it."

"But I *am* interested in it, and it amuses me. Just think, for example, I found a snapshot of you and two other young men all dressed up as Fascists."

"Left over from my student days," I said. "Thanks for reminding me about it. I'd better put it under lock and key."

"Ahah," she exclaimed. "See there, you repudiate the past."

"On the contrary. The fact is, one of those two boys is a bigwig in the extreme rightist party and that picture would upset him, if it fell into the wrong hands. We're enemies now, but I still wouldn't like it to happen."

"Why not, if he's your enemy?"

"Because we had been friends since we were so tall, and I respect everything that belongs to my childhood."

Jo shook her head and continued with her inspection. "So who is this little girl with big round eyes that looks like Michelone?"

"It's me at the age of five," I said.

This information cheered her up. "Are you telling me that at the age of five you wore your hair like a Beatle and long gowns with lace collars?"

"Sure. In those days all children, even past the age of five, wore skirts. A marvelous style—you got dressed and un-dressed in three seconds, because all you were wearing was an identification tag and this skirt. That was the way it was out in the villages. In the morning, mamma washed the baby's face with a little fresh water and laundry soap, pulled on this gown, gave him a crust of bread, and put him outside to play. In those days you didn't have cars, so the streets, squares, and banks of the river all belonged to the children. However, before letting her child run off, the mamma would pin the back hem of the skirt up as high as his shoulders with a safety pin, so the kid would run around with the bottom half of his backside in the open air and in case of emergency all he'd have to do is squat and nothing got dirty."

"How primitive," Jo said with disdain.

"And why? This happened when the weather was nice and the little ones could go outside. Then the roads were covered with at least ten centimeters of white dust, and in summertime it was a delicious sensation to sit down in the soft, hot dust. I suppose you won't believe this, Jo, but that pleasant warmth still cheers me now. And when the sun beat down on the Valley at its hottest it was wonderful to be able to sit in the fresh wet sand on the banks of the river, leaving your prints behind."

"Poor kids!" Jo exclaimed.

"Today's kids are the ones to feel sorry for—brought up on balanced diets like chickens and hogs, forced to wear pants the moment they're born, and at the age of four forced to masquerade as grown men, with long pants, ties, wrist-watches, and, half the time, a transistor radio or record player hung around their necks. Oh yes, a vast improvement, today's way of bringing up children."

Just then Margherita came into the room. "Nobody is older than the old man who praises the ignorant, primitive customs of his childhood. Modern mothers know what they are doing."

"Modern mothers only too often treat their children the same way those disgusting women with the pink poodles make them sleep on cute little doggy beds and wear wool coats in the wintertime, complete with bonnets and booties and plushy BVD's."

"We were talking about children, not about poodles!" Jo exclaimed. "Imagine if Michelone were forced to wear a skirt with the curtain raised in the rear. Imagine it!"

"That's exactly what I'm imagining."

All grandparents have projects for their grandchildren. After having watched the projects they had planned for their own children fail miserably, they want to try again with the grandchildren. But almost inevitably death steps in and saves the grandparents from still another disappointment. Naturally I think about seeing Michelone dressed up the way I was as a baby. To avenge, through him, all the poor babies who have been vexed and inhibited by modern science and styles. And above all, to relive through him my distant and blissful childhood. To see him walk barefoot in the dust. Well, there isn't any dust these days. But you can buy it by the truckload, olive-press dust, which is the same as the dust in my childhood. I have a drive on my property; I could transform it into a stretch of dusty country road. Of course, seeing him in a corduroy dress with his little fanny tinted with dust would be like seeing myself again. And certainly I would be able to see my grandmother Filomena again, and hear her whistle.

I should explain that I'm not my mother's son, but rather my great-grandmother's, my mother's mother's mother's son. She was one of those little old ladies who are all skin and bones, used as the models for grandmothers in fairy tales.

She was frightening, and if I took too long on my rounds she would come after me, and as soon as she spotted me she would whistle. The note was long, high, and as piercing as the blade of a dagger. My reaction to this whistle was to perform the scene of Tamed Rebellion—to try to escape and then come back, with my head hanging in shame, crushed under the thumb of her fierce authority. I would approach her trembling and stand as if nailed to the spot, while she would take from behind her back a twig and flail at my legs with it. I always had an insane urge to laugh, because the twig tickled my legs but instead I was meant to cry. So I cried. I was only a small child, but I knew how to give her some satisfaction, poor thing!

How many times did I hear that whistle! She died at the age of eighty-six but she never abandoned me in difficult moments. The last time I saw her was in September 1945, when I came back from the concentration camp. There was no transportation to take me home from the city, so I headed for the country on foot, a knapsack full of tatters on my back. I left the country highway just as twilight was setting in, and there in the middle of the rocky and lonesome road a shattering doubt crept into my mind: I hadn't had any news from my family for over a year, and the war had passed right by our house. Would I find them all still there? Some of them? None?

And only then, when the entire adventure was over, I became afraid and I slumped down on the bank of the ditch nearby and cowered like a ragamuffin.

Suddenly I heard her whistle and whipped my head around to look. There she was at the end of the road, standing under the big poplar in front of our house. She waved her cane in the air menacingly and I got up and ran as fast as I could down the drive to our house.

The house was still standing, and inside it, everybody was safe and sound. Actually, more than everybody, because there waiting for me was the future mother of Michelone, whom I hadn't yet seen because she had arrived two months after I left.

Of course if Michelone were to dress up in a corduroy frock, his great-great-grandmother would be bound to come back to earth to see him. But if I were so much as to propose such a thing they'd pack me off to an insane asylum. It's best to drop the subject.

Jo looked at the old photograph and then said: "Let's be honest. As a baby girl he was dreadful, but as a baby boy he was a beauty!"

"Pity it wore off growing up," sighed Margherita.

The Criminal

☼

Hey," Jo said treacherously one afternoon, "what would you do if you won 200 million lire on the Football Pool?"

Each of us has, jealously hidden away in his heart, a secret project at which he churns away mentally during every spare moment. Even I have one, and since it's the style nowadays to tell all your secrets in books, I confessed my plan to Jo.

"I'd organize a sort of coup. I met a man in jail who works in Milan and I'd give him charge of the whole deal. He's a nice fellow, a man of action, just right for the job."

"One of those gangsters with a Luger in a shoulder holster?" she asked, bright-eyed with curiosity.

"Who said anything about a Luger! This fellow is a professional thief, and professional thieves don't ever carry arms. Only dilettantes do, thinking they can make up for lack of brains by wearing a firearm. Jo, you should be careful what you believe in those movies and detective stories of yours. A rod is only for nitwits. In the criminal hierarchy, first place goes to the swindler or con-man who works showing his face and whose only weapons are intelligence, foxiness, imagination, and good psychology. Next comes the serious professional thief, who works alone on sure things, in rich homes, businesses, offices, warehouses. Then comes the pickpocket, then the car thief, then the bicycle thief, then the chicken thief—the latter must be considered sentimentalists, still plying their old trades in the age of interplanetary travel and billion-dollar fortunes. Next down on the list is the stool-pigeon and way down at the very bottom, the least worthy and respectable, comes the armed robber. The fellow I'm talking about is a serious professional thief. And he's very friendly toward me because I helped him through a tremendous spiritual crisis."

"I know!" Jo exclaimed. "He was plagued with remorse."

"Correct. For six months he'd been employed as a chauffeur by a family of millionaires who trusted him completely and unconditionally. Money, jewelry, old masters, silver and gold plate—everything was put right under his nose. 'All I had to do was reach out and shovel it in my pocket!" he'd whimper to me. 'Why? Why didn't I?' He couldn't forgive himself."

"And you pulled him out of this tailspin?" she snickered.

"Jo, it was no laughing matter. This anxiety of his wasn't caused by pain of remorse for something terrible he'd done but because he simply couldn't understand why he hadn't acted true to form. So I said to him, 'Lucky, if you bumped into Leonardo painting the picture of Mona Lisa you'd ask him why, instead of slaving away with so many brushes and colors, he didn't just take her photograph and let it go at that.' His answer was that even though he wasn't an art expert he wouldn't say anything that stupid. So I spouted the logical moral to the story: 'Lucky, a common fool can

take a photograph or drop in his pocket a jewel that some
unwatchful nitwit leaves around. But only an artistic genius
could have painted the Mona Lisa, and you too, in your own
field, are an artistic genius.' "

"Lucky's a nice name," Jo pointed out. "It has a nice
Chicago ring to it. What was he in jail for?"

"He'd quit his job as a chauffeur to return to the greener
pastures of his old profession. But he'd organized a little
gang, with two dolts, to work the bars and tobacconists on
the outskirts of Parma. A two-bit operation in which he
behaved like an infant because, apart from cigarettes and
postage stamps, Lucky had taken to snatching nougat
candies, and afterward, instead of keeping his mind on
driving the car, he was busy trying to pry the nougat out of
his teeth, and you know how easy it is to hang up on a
wayside post when you're driving with only one hand. Naturally he managed to do just that. But he was a smart lad and
I told him that a fellow with his talents shouldn't waste his
time stealing candies and other nonsense from tobacconists.
'You're the jewelry store type,' I told him. 'It's never a sure
thing with jewelry stores,' he said. 'I know one in Cremona
that's clean as a whistle and I know how to get in too,' I
answered, joking. We never spoke of it again, I was released,
and two years later, I got a letter from Lucky saying 'I'm all
set for the Cremona caper.' "

Jo shook her head. "You say he is intelligent, but I don't
see how he can be if he didn't understand you were joking!"

"Jo," I explained, "Lucky had a lot of respect for me.
What he probably thought was that I had given up the
stupid path I'd had to follow because of my misguided
education, and as a result of having been exposed to the

salutory atmosphere and the proper element of society in the prison, my true nature of crook had risen to the surface. Like those old paintings that on the surface show a garden-variety saint but it's only an overpainting, and in scraping off the crust laid on by an unknown hack, an extraordinary Titian or Velásquez jumps out. But I must say, Lucky's letter sorely tempted me."

"Now I understand," the girl said. "I can see that prison must have been a beautiful experience for you."

"I'd say a rather ugly experience, in fact."

"Did they treat you badly?"

"Not really. I was considered a common criminal and they don't treat common criminals badly. Which is why, every time a general amnesty frees them, they're back in stir in a few days."

"Doubtless you ran across people who are in jail not because they're bad but because they're victims of social justice?"

"Certainly," I answered. "The prison guards."

"Oh," she said. "Did they make life hard for you?"

"No, except for the warden. He gave me a miserable time!"

Margherita started to laugh: "Was it really him?"

"And nobody else!" I asserted. "All you have to do is take one look at his face and you know the type."

Margherita handed Jo the weekly she was reading, open to the appropriate page, on which there was a photograph and a headline that read: *I Was the Warden of Ciano Prison.* The picture was of a Marshal in the Prison Guard Corps. "There he is," she said.

Jo studied the photograph and then said unhesitantly:

"He doesn't seem at all evil-looking. In fact he looks like a perfect gentleman."

"Not only that, he *is* a perfect gentleman. That was the trouble."

"How could it be a trouble?" Margherita asked, astonished.

"Easily! I was in there gagging on the newspapers who were writing all manner of vile things about me and I couldn't answer back. I would have tried to send out some kind of clandestine message or an article, since even if I wasn't allowed to read it my magazine was still being published. But how could I carry on such traffic under the nose of a decent chap like that? Margherita, do you remember the trouble he got into when some photographer climbed up to the roof of the building across the street to get a telephoto shot of me while I was saying hello to you, then sold the picture to Biagi who published it in the magazine?"

"Of course I remember," Margherita said.

"So what's wrong with that?" Jo demanded. "Didn't people know you were in prison?"

"Sure, even the dogs and cats knew. That's why I said the warden made life difficult for me. Jo, there's always trouble if in certain situations you find a trustworthy person."

Jo meditated on my sour observation and then said, "That's all well and good, but you still haven't told me what coup you would organize with Lucky if 200 million lire suddenly fell into your lap."

"A fantastic stroke of genius: I'd ask him to swipe all the early issues from the archives of the *Corriere dei Piccoli.*"

Jo looked at me dumbfounded. She said she didn't understand.

"Don't you understand what it would mean to me to be

able to leaf through the crumbling old issues of that little paper in the privacy of my own home? That newspaper was the first piece of printing I ever saw and it kept me company throughout my childhood. I'd be able to find again, stuck to those ancient pages, my first thoughts, my first reasonings, my first sensations. I know it. In the proper atmosphere, seeing again certain figures, certain colors, I would be able to hear again the voices of my great-grandmother Filomena, my mother, my father. A hundred, a thousand remembrances buried in the dark warehouse of memory would reawaken. Our mind remembers everything, provided it is given the proper conditions for remembering. Think, Jo, why it is when you see a certain landscape illumined by a certain light you will say, 'I've seen this before!' whereas the fact is you've never seen the place before in your life, only perhaps some ancestor of yours has hundreds of years ago?"

"Do things like this happen to him often?" the girl asked Margherita.

"They don't happen just to me. I think it's called atavistic memory. It happened to me the first time I saw Poland. Then, years later, I was told that some distant ancestors of mine came from Poland."

"A less distant ancestor of his, who was also named Giovanni, held up the parish priest and was sentenced to run around in circles forever," Margherita interrupted, laughing.

Jo shook her head sadly. "Given your ancestors and your friendship with Lucky," she said judiciously, "let's hope you don't win the Football Pool."

"I give up!" I said in exactly the same tone and spirit as Garibaldi once said "I obey!"

Pedestrians Are Crazy

✵

It was a marvelous night, I felt strong, calm, rested, I had nothing to carry, I had no urgent commitments, so instead of waiting for a train to take me north, I decided to negotiate the thirty or so kilometers on foot.

These days, to go from place to place on foot is a luxury only millionaires can afford and that night I felt young, therefore very rich. Coming out of the train station, I walked along at a good clip, and as soon as I could, I left the big highway, covered with stinking, cinder-billowing diesel vans, and took off down the country road.

There's little to say about it: you poor people condemned forever to travel by car or airplane, at the speed of the wind or of sound, can't imagine the joy it is for a man to be able to travel using the only means provided him by nature and walk at his own speed.

The horse moves at the speed of a horse, the dog, cat, lamb, travel at the speed of dogs, cats, and lambs respectively, and they all know it and derive from it great benefits to their physical and mental well-being. Have you ever met a dog or a horse compelled to see a psychiatrist?

Thirty kilometers on foot, down familiar country roads, in

a magical May night—that's my idea of a marvelous way to spend your free time. I was thinking of how I would enjoy, second by second, the miraculous sight of the sunrise and the rebirth of colors.

The turbine rhythm and the failure of a foolish life that makes man the slave of numberless machines has stolen from him the pleasure of hearing his own footsteps. It's a music far superior to any Rock beat, with entrancing effects when one passes a cluster of silent houses and arouses echoes nesting in the old walls and courtyards.

Tap, tap, tap . . . how fine my leather soles sound as they hit the asphalt hardened by the brisk night air. The scansion of my walk blossoms into faint wisps of martial airs that rise up from the depths of my memory. With the tunes vague dreams of glory revive.

But Progress is always lurking somewhere. A rumbling cuts across my listening and the whole vision goes up in smoke. I inch over to the edge of an irrigation ditch, but the intruder has already spotted me. He passes me and then squeals to a halt. The light of an electric torch blinds me.

It turns out to be a patrol car. One of them asks me for my papers and I hand him my identification.

"Where are you coming from? Where are you headed?"

I say I'm coming from Parma and going home.

"But that's more than thirty kilometers," they object.

"Thirty-three," I inform them.

"And how do you come to be walking thirty-three kilometers on foot?"

I explain that I got off at the wrong railroad station.

"Ahah! And you didn't have enough money for another train ticket."

Stupidly, I show them a wad of 10,000-lire notes. The fact that a man loaded with money should be traveling thirty-three kilometers on foot strikes them as being very suspicious.

"How did you come by such a lot of money?"

"I cashed a check at the bank. A check just like these." Out of my pocket I pull a checkbook with my name printed all over it. I show them an envelope containing a paycheck from the newspaper which I stupidly forgot to deposit this afternoon. Minute by minute the case is becoming more suspicious to them. I'm not too pleasant-looking and pretty shabbily dressed, but I don't look like an armed bandit. In any case, armed bandits don't carry around checkbooks—they simply hold out a gun and the money goes into their other hand. And given my respectable age and my mustache, I don't really look like the kind of man who kills his wife in a fit of jealousy and spends the rest of the night running away from remorse.

They stick the electric torch right under my nose, presumably to check whether my mustache is real. They decide it is real and doesn't even give the impression of a disguised international spy. I show them a few more documents and the sergeant studies them carefully and hands them back.

"Okay, everything's in order," he admits. "But you still haven't told us what you're doing here, in open country, at one A.M."

"I'm going home . . ."

"Here we go again!" he says, annoyed. "A normal human being with your resources doesn't walk thirty-three kilometers in the middle of the night!"

"I want to rest a little," I explain foolishly. But I mean it, because, for a poor soul condemned to spend all his time seated at a little table, or in a car, or curled up in bed, the only way to rest is to stand right up on your legs and use them. But naturally they misinterpret my answer.

"Don't play the comedian and answer my question. How do you explain your being here?"

It's always hard to make yourself believed when you're telling the purest, tritest truth. I attempt no more than to spread my arms wide and the sergeant says nastily, "Why are you wasting our time like this? Come now, tell us the truth!"

At that point a jeep arrived and an officer got out. The sergeant explained the situation to him in whispers. Then he introduced the case in point by shining the ubiquitous light in my face.

The officer burst out laughing and asked me, very amused, how I'd let myself get caught prowling around at night in the middle of the countryside with all this suspicious evidence on me. We had known each other for years. He told me he had to go past my neighborhood anyway and offered me a ride home.

"Thanks," I answered, "but I'd rather keep on walking. That is, providing there isn't some law against it."

"You're free to go wherever you choose," he said, "but don't be surprised if another patrol car stops you. In this motorized age, when even chicken thieves do their business riding in Giuliettas, a person who tours around at night on foot is highly suspect. Even more so since you're alone."

He was right too; in the age of the herd a man by himself is considered abnormal. But I'd made up my mind: even at the risk of being mistaken for a man of principle, I was going ahead on foot. The officer looked at me worriedly, shaking his head, then wished me a good trip and drove off after the patrol car.

It was a miraculous night and I walked on, full of enthusiasm, toward the dawn. I wasn't alone, either, for I had found all of myself again. It's incredible how clearly one can see one's own life, walking alone in the dark of night.

I walked along quietly for more than an hour; then a car came and stopped in front of me.

"Do you mind telling me what you think you're doing here at three in the morning?"

I recognized Margherita's voice and answered very bitterly, "Why don't *you* tell *me* what you think you're doing here instead of being in bed!"

"Well," she answered. "*Should* I be in bed, after a police officer rings up to say that my miserable husband is wandering around on foot in the deserted countryside acting like a madman? Giovanni, now if you're going to get drunk, couldn't you please arrange to do it without making a public spectacle of yourself in the streets?"

"I haven't touched a drop and I'm not making a spectacle of myself! All I want is simply to walk!"

Then Jo piped up. "Listen, you. Fight it out later. Now get in and cut it out because I'm sleepy."

I said, in that case they could just get out of my way. "I want to walk on and watch the sun come up!"

"You can watch it out of the window of your room," Margherita said firmly. "Either you get in or I start to shriek."

We were close by a cluster of houses, so I had to get in.

Once home Margherita asked me sweetly if she should call the doctor.

"Doctor my foot!" Jo put in. "What he needs is a psychiatrist. Maybe you'd better ring the insane asylum."

Roaring like a bull, I ran to lock myself in my pigeon-coop.

All Hail, Blackface!

☼

Get my bicycle ready," I said the next morning to Jo. "Check the tires and if necessary feed them some air. I have to go to Fidenza to mail something."

Our domestic assistant gazed at me, astonished and indignant. "With all the machines you have tucked away in the garage, you want to make a thirty-kilometer trip, fifteen there, fifteen back, on a *bicycle?*"

"Very good arithmetic."

"Oh dear," she tittered. "I'd forgotten you were hung up on bicycles."

"It's not just me," I answered. "If you look at yesterday's *Corriere,* you'll see that in America there are sixty million bicycles in use, six million of which were sold this year. They calculate that in ten years, bicycle sales will rise to ten million per year. The phenomenon is so important that the Government has budgeted 180 million dollars per year for the next twenty years for building pathways reserved for bicyclists."

"I read all about it," she said. "The Americans are an unfortunate lot. The minute the news got out that the celebrated Dr. White had recommended that Eisenhower take up cycling to improve his heart condition, the whole nation jumped on bicycles."

"And went on the bottle too," Margherita added perfidiously. "Evidently this doctor also proclaimed that whisky was a powerful agent for dilating the blood vessels, hence very good for clearing up circulatory congestion. Naturally there have been a lot of silly old men quaffing down whisky as if it were mineral water, thereby ruining stomach and liver to the point where they could only drink orange squash . . ."

"We were talking about bicycles, not alcoholics," I interrupted her, very salty, since it makes me angry to hear underhanded remarks about people of my acquaintance, particularly if they happen to be me.

Jo started to laugh. "Look at him, so anti-American, and here he is, behaving exactly like an American—Americans being the sort of people who, if you explained the healthful qualities of clay, would take up drinking juice made of bricks and tiles in the morning."

"What do you mean, American!" I shouted. "The bicycle is a European invention. It was born in Paris a year after the Bastille fell and is without question the most important product of the French revolution. And now, not only in America but also in Europe, the bicycle is having a triumphant renascence, because last year they sold 900,000 bicycles in France alone."

"You've already made your speech about bicycle sales and there's no point in repeating it," Jo said firmly. "What I find laughable is that, suddenly because there's a boom in bicycle sales abroad, you have to make a thirty-kilometer trip just to put a letter in the box. Give me the letter—I'll take it in the car."

"That won't do," Margherita said. "You don't have 'smoker's leg,' he does."

"Now what sort of foolishness is this 'smoker's leg'?" the girl asked.

"You know, he's a comic writer and invents charming diseases like 'athlete's toe' and 'laundress's knee.' Still, I don't know what he finds so amusing about the fact that, given the poor circulation of blood poisoned by nicotine, one of his legs doesn't work any more and eventually will have to be amputated."

Jo shook her head. "Wouldn't it be simpler if he quit smoking? It doesn't seem to me that the ideal cure for 'smoker's leg' is a thirty-kilometer bicycle trip, particularly when he suffers acutely from 'writer's fanny.' "

"There's no such disease!" I protested indignantly.

"Wait to say that until you've done the thirty kilometers by bicycle," she answered. "Come on, forget the bicycle. What car do you want me to get out—the Bianchina, the Millecento, or the Millecinquecento?"

"No! I want my bicycle!" I shouted furiously, stamping the foot attached to my "smoker's leg" against the pavement angrily.

"Okay," Jo said going out. "But you've got a couple of screws loose, I'll say that."

I didn't take offense. Jo doesn't understand. Jo is a representative of the Prosperity Generation for whom the automobile is the machine created as a substitute for the legs in all instances except dancing. The Prosperity Generation might even be symbolized by a motorized centaur: that is, a being who is human from the head to the waist and automobile from the waist down. Jo's way of thinking doesn't surprise me. Even I, twenty-eight years ago, when I bought my first car, was prey to the sacred fury that today besets millions upon millions of Italians.

It had been a few years since I had moved to Milan, and life was marvelously simple. If, for example, Margherita told me to go buy something at the drugstore, all I had to do was walk down the stairs from our fifth-floor apartment, cross the street, go inside the drugstore, all of fifty meters from the door of my building, and then come home. It took four minutes.

Once I had the car, however, the project became infinitely complicated. Having negotiated the stairs from the fifth floor to the ground floor, I had to trek about a kilometer to the garage on via Noë where I kept the Millecento. There, having solved the reasonably complex problem of extricating the Millecento from the pile of other cars, I would seat myself behind the steering wheel and aim toward the drugstore. But inevitably the street would be so packed with bicycle vans, carts, vendors, and knife-sharpeners that I would have to drive over to a square about half a kilometer away to park the car. I walked 500 meters to the drugstore, bought whatever it was, walked 500 meters back to the car (total: one kilometer) parked in the square, and drove to the garage on via Noë. Then I walked home. Sum total: three kilometers on foot and three kilometers by car to make a trip of 100 meters.

At this point one of you people is bound to say: "Regardless of what things are like now, it's clear that in 1938 you were a first-class idiot."

That's not so. In 1938 I was a normal person, but I'd just conquered the automobile. This was a fabulous achievement thirty years ago for a peasant from the Valley near Parma who had drifted into Milan with nothing but a tattered umbrella and unlimited stubbornness. I had conquered the automobile and it was unthinkable not to use it for my most minor movements. Here I had the car; of course I had to use it. Otherwise why buy it in the first place? I had promoted myself from miserable worm-pedestrian to auto-owner. An auto-owner, to earn his new title, must perform all movements in his automobile. What about those three kilometers on foot, you ask? The answer is, I didn't walk them in the capacity of worm-pedestrian but rather as an auto-owner on his way to claiming his automobile. I would have fallen back into the routine of miserable worm-pedestrian if I had condescended to negotiate the 100-meter trip on foot. Also we are talking about 1938, when the auto-owner was a phenomenon, a loner. These days the auto-owner sends a representative to the Senate, there are reams of publications to keep him apprised of everything happening in the realm of automobiles; there are books to inform you of your rights and privileges as an auto-owner. Today the auto-owner possesses pride, dignity, and class-consciousness. Also, a car is representative of Prosperity; it's the tangible proof of the achievement of Prosperity and therefore must be used everywhere and at all times. An auto-owner who does not use his car at all times and everywhere must feel like a slave who, once liberated, orders his chains welded to his wrists and ankles again and walks around thus shackled.

How many people are sincerely persuaded that as soon as

they are seated behind the steering wheel of their cars they automatically become "somebody"? Millions and millions of parvenu auto-owners in Italy, all of whom feel naked if they have to walk anywhere. Like the supreme commander of the Joint Chiefs of Staff who is suddenly demoted to latrine orderly.

That's the way things are and people risk their lives in the defense of their status as motorists. But there's nothing to worry about; after a certain length of time, a motorist comes to realize that even if he's not behind the wheel of a car, he's still a respectable human being. He becomes aware that an automobile used when it's not necessary is a pain in the neck. He might even reach the point of hating cars, which are actually respectable pieces of machinery when used properly. But look at what is happening in the United States, where they've come to have a car for every single inhabitant, young or old, male or female: they've suddenly rediscovered the bicycle. Just like the man who runs through every conceivable style of raincoat and suddenly rediscovers the umbrella.

To make a long story short, I reached Fidenza on my trusty Dei in the same amount of time it takes the racer Adorni to ride from Bologna to Piacenza. Unfortunately, however, the kilometers going back seemed considerably longer (about 2,500 meters longer), and just as that wretch Jo had predicted, "writer's fanny" set in with a vengeance. But I went on undaunted, churning away at the pedals. Soon a little diesel pickup passed me on the right and slowed down to keep up with me.

"Now if I were you I'd throw the damn bike in the back here and get inside," the driver said, hanging her head out the window.

I shook my head violently.

"Well, at least grab a hold, then," the girl said.

I didn't give her the answer she deserved because a cubic inch of breath is worth a cubic inch of gold in certain situations. A bicyclist who grabs hold of a truck is about as low as the hunter who kills a cat and takes it home like an African pelt.

"Your wife ordered me to pack you into this truck even if I have to use force," Jo shouted menacingly.

"Beat it!" I shouted back. "Go on, move off and leave me some room to breathe!"

I pulled around behind the pickup, grabbed onto one of the pinions, and threw myself into the chase body and soul. The diesel's process of combustion was less than tidy and it belched out a dense, sticky black smoke. Hence it's not surprising that Margherita, on seeing me arrive, greeted me with the cheerful cry: "Hail, Blackface!"

I found that touching and, dismounting from the bicycle, I thought about Italy in Africa and felt like a remnant of the Empire.

Suspense

November. Afternoon. It's raining. It's raining after a long dry spell and the farmer isn't worried any more about his wheat; now that there's water, the seed will germinate.

But the farmer still isn't happy because he's plagued by a nagging thought: it's raining, but not just on *his* wheatfields. It's raining on other farmers' wheatfields too.

Men are making trips to the moon (that's to tell you how the world has changed) but the farmer always stays the same. He's rugged, all right, and can put up with any kind of hardship. What he can't take, though, is good things that happen to other people.

So, it's raining. A huge log is roaring in the fireplace. Stretched out comfortably in my plushy rocking chair, I'm enjoying the fire and keeping an eye on my chestnuts as they slowly roast in a little pan with holes in the bottom.

After a while I'll take the chestnuts out of the fire and wrap them up in a damp cloth to make them softer.

Eleven sparkling eyes attentively follow the chestnut operation. (Now you're asking, How come *eleven* eyes, when there are only two children in the room and each of them has a perfectly normal set of *two* eyes? Well, I don't know.

There are certain sensations that you can't explain. If the number bothers you, raise the number to twelve—no less than three pairs per head, because here we're not talking about ordinary children but of the Phenomenon and Michelone, grandchildren by profession.)

Anyhow, this is what we have: a rainy November afternoon, a nice crackling fire, some chestnuts, a grandfather with his grandchildren. I take a lightning step fifty years backward in time and find myself the protagonist of a picture out of my third-grade reader, *My House, My Country*. (Imagine what any child of today would say about that title!)

Like a fool, I described the picture in my third-grade reader to my audience.

"Oh, what a romantic picture!" Margherita said, while Jo collapsed with laughter. "However, to be perfect, the little grandfather should be wearing quilted slippers, a skull-cap on his bald head, and telling fairy tales to his dear little grandchildren."

"Well, I'm not a 'little grandfather,' " I said resentfully. "Furthermore, I'm not bald and I don't know how to tell fairy tales to dear little grandchildren!"

"That's not true!" said Michelone's wicked mother, who was drifting around the room. "You told us some wonderful stories and I've never forgotten them."

I remembered them vividly too and in a thunderous voice I cried, "No! We're not going through that again!"

The stuff of twenty years ago; I was still living in Milan and Italy had begun its struggle to be reborn, which consisted of rebuilding destroyed houses and tearing down whatever was left of our spiritual heritage.

Then Michelone's mother was a tiny infant and I called her Passionaria, appropriately, considering her character. And Albertino, the Phenomenon's father, was a quiet, reserved little boy who looked like something out of a boy's magazine.

It's a well-known fact that it's much easier to write a 600-page novel than a 6-page story. And very often, you could derive a 600-page novel out of a 6-page story, but you'd never be able to get 6 decent pages worth of story out of a 600-page novel.

One night the two children refused to go to sleep, so being an ignoramus, I said: "Once upon a time, there was a little boy named Kakokino . . ."

It was a stupid name, but it made an impression. I was twenty years younger and scrounged a living writing novels and short stories. It wasn't difficult to dredge up Kakokino and launch his first romantic adventure.

I didn't finish the story of Kakokino the first night. I dropped him in a tight spot and left the ending for the next installment.

A few days later, naturally, they demanded that I continue the story of Kakokino. Thus it was that I found myself inextricably entangled in a vicious plot to destroy my peace of mind. Every two or three evenings I had to put Kakokino to work. And it wasn't easy, because inevitably I ended every installment with Kakokino in a worse bind than the one before.

Finally, in desperation, I abandoned Kakokino in the

middle of a storm at sea, clinging for dear life to a raft that was about to founder and sink.

It was an ugly situation, particularly because in my stories I stringently refused to allow any external interventions, dei ex machina, Fate with her Magic wand, and other such rubbish.

Then as now, given my working system (which consists of a total lack of system), I slept in a tiny room attached to my study. Around midnight, Passionaria showed up. She woke me and demanded to know how Kakokino was going to save himself. She said just thinking about the poor wretch kept her from sleeping.

"Day after tomorrow you'll know," I answered.

It wasn't easy to get Kakokino out of his jams and I had to play for time. But she swore to me to keep it to herself, and so to get rid of her I said, "All I can tell you is that he will save himself and will become the chief of a tribe of savages."

That sent her on her way. An hour later, Margherita shook my shoulder and when my eyes were open said, "Giovanni, tell me how that fool Kakokino is going to get out of the storm you've left him in."

"I already told your daughter."

"That's why I'm asking you. Her brother is dying to know too and she's managed to put the squeeze on him for all his crayons, three coloring books, and the electric train. She says she won't tell until he gives her his entire collection of marbles. They've been fighting for an hour and I can't sleep."

"Margherita," I said, "I told the girl any old thing to get

her out of my hair. The truth is, I really don't know how I'm going to get Kakokino out of this jam."

"You vile reprobate!" she howled. "You put a poor little boy in dire tribulation and you don't know how you're going to get him out of it!"

"Oh yes I do!" I said, losing my temper. "This time I'm going to drown the little monster and, God willing, that will be the end of this nonsense!"

"Would you have the courage to do something that evil? Characters in stories are like children: once you bring them into the world, you've got to take care of them. Now that the children like Kakokino so much, how can you think of killing him, you murderer?"

"Margherita, I've already made up forty installments and I refuse to go on wracking my brains for that imbecile. I'll kill him!"

"Ahah, so you're going to be just like those ancient storytellers who let the children get eaten up by ogres or stick them in witches' brew to boil. You're going to be one of those monsters who solves everything by murdering. Well, just remember that stories aren't meant to terrorize children."

"Okay," I said. "I won't kill him. But this time he's going to break at least a leg, an arm, and six ribs."

Kakokino saved himself from the storm at sea, but in the following adventure he fell from a balcony and had to be taken to the hospital and treated for multiple fractures.

"Now we're going to let him rest," I told them. "Then, when he gets well, we'll put him to work again."

Thus I freed myself from Kakokino, because certain

things happened and certain changes took place that made them forget about Kakokino.

"The story!" the Phenomenon hissed.

"The story!" Michelone hissed.

"What story?" I growled bad-humoredly.

"The one about Kakokino," Michelone explained. "Mamma said Kakokino was in hospital, but he's all better now."

I whirled around to face Michelone's wicked mother. "Kakokino!" I roared. "How did they find out about that monster!"

"I told them. I described him and they liked him very much. I explained that he was in the hospital. But now that twenty years have gone by, I'm sure he's well again. Apart from the fact that I'd like to know how the story ends myself."

Twenty years later: Kakokino comes out of the hospital, younger and more foolish than before, and takes up his former adventuresome life. I'm twenty years older and as if that weren't enough, Michelone and the Phenomenon belong to the new generation, that of ceaseless demand.

Kakokino, who twenty years ago worked alone, now works with a gang. The Phenomenon has demanded that a cat, a little sparrow, a dog, and a lamb join forces with him. Meanwhile Michelone demands that a horse be taken along too. I wonder if anybody knows how difficult it is to work a horse into a story. But Michelone wants it that way. He got excited about a picture that appeared in some magazine of the epic charge of the Cossacks against the Bolsheviks' murderous machine guns.

I told Michelone the horses won, but of course it's not true.

The 100,000-Lira Bill

✵

The owner of a bookstore in Milan wrote to tell me that he had come into possession of a collection of old numbers of an illustrated magazine that would probably be of interest to me; so I decided to make a flying visit to Milan. I left in my jalopy one Saturday morning, and everything went splendidly until I was about twenty kilometers from Milan, when I suddenly realized I was down to two drops of gasoline. I stopped at the first station I could find to have the tank filled.

While the attendant filled it up I got out my money to pay. Or rather I got out my wallet which presumably had enough small change in it to pay for a few gallons of gas; and then I thought of Margherita.

Let's be frank: Margherita isn't one of those notorious women who claims it's her right and duty to inspect her husband's wallet to draw out the funds necessary to balance the family budget. Inspired by the admirable motive of not wanting to worry their husbands with distasteful financial discussions, these women don't say a word about what they siphon off, and therefore from time to time their good intentions can prove singularly inconvenient.

Margherita not only inspects my coin purse in which I keep petty cash—1,000- and 500-lira notes as well as 100-, 50-, 20-, 10-, and 5-lira pieces—but whenever it's necessary for her to remove something from my wallet, where I keep bills of larger denomination, she leaves a little note: "IOU 10,000; 20,000 withdrawn 10/16 for household expenses, etc. etc."

I opened the coin purse, as I said, and immediately thought of Margherita, because what I found was a lot of 20-, 10-, and 5-lira coins, which even a Chinaman knows won't buy you so much as a stick of chewing gum.

Not losing hope, I immediately looked in my wallet, where there was bound to be some money. Instead I found this interesting communication: "Couldn't make change for bill you gave me Thurs. Took 90,000 in paper money and 10,000 in small change."

Considering the fact that the excellent creature had left a brand-new 100,000-lira bill in my wallet, you might consider the entire operation administratively unexceptionable.

Unhappily, when I handed the attendant the 100,000-lira bill, he shook his head and told me to stop kidding around. Then he added his private thoughts about smart-alecks who offer to pay for six gallons of gasoline with 100,000-lira bills. Of course the man wasn't entirely without justification, so I handed him the little note Margherita had left me. He read it carefully and handed it back.

"All I can do for you, sir," he said, "is testify on your behalf when they try you for killing your wife."

I laboriously counted out the small change in my coin purse and figured that it was enough to pay for a gallon and a half of gas.

"Very good," the man said sarcastically. "A gallon and a half is yours and you give me back four and a half."

He made me move the car so as not to obstruct traffic, took the keys from the dashboard and put them in his pocket, and handed me a siphon and a plastic pail with measuring marks.

"Have at it," he said. "When the pail is full up to this line which says '4½'," he explained, "you're all set. Of course you'll be careful, since any gas you spill belongs to you, not me."

Truthfully, I didn't lose a drop, because anything that didn't trickle into the pail, my pants soaked up. But eventually this part of the story ended and I got back on the road.

I arrived in Milan around eleven. I easily found the bookshop—with its window grill pulled down and a sign saying: "Closed owing to the flu." There was nothing for it but to go home. But try as I might I couldn't find a gas station that would take the 100,000-lira bill in payment for the full tank of gas. Now it was noon, so I went inside a restaurant, ate a modest lunch, and paid with the 100,000-lira note. The waiter came back after a short time and said the cashier didn't have change for me and asked me to pay with a bill of smaller denomination. I explained that it wasn't possible for me to do so, and so the proprietor of the restaurant made his appearance. He was a perfectly reasonable man. He too got to read the little note Margherita had left in my wallet. He agreed that women have very special brains and I begged him to consider my plight and help me out.

"If you really can't give me change for it, will you at least take a check?"

"All right," he said. "You can give me a check. It's always smarter to stand a loss of 2,500 lire than one of 100,000."

"I'll write it for 5,000," I said hesitantly. "You give me 2,500 in change, so I can get a few drops of gas to get home on."

"No," he said shortly. "Be grateful for the meal."

I must have some friends in Milan, I thought; but how to fish them out of the quagmire of memory? I puttered around the city searching for some inspiration, but all I managed to do was empty the tank of what gas it had. Fortunately I found a garage that accepted the car in return for a proper receipt.

But even on foot I wasn't able to dredge up an inspiration to get me out of this jam. Night fell, and finally I rebelled. "I'm an honest man," I said. "I have 100,000 lire in my pocket, which I earned through my own sweat and toil. I regularly pay a fat wad of taxes, I have a steady job, a house, some property, and a bank account. I have the God-given right to eat a meal, get my car back, fill my tank with gas, phone up Margherita and tell her exactly what I think of her, and, finally, to go home!"

I went straight to what I knew was the most expensive restaurant in the city, ordered a regal meal and, for a wine, vintage champagne. I was cognizant of my God-given rights, but I needed to refuel myself.

The bill came to a sturdy sum—but even a state of severe shock is somewhat softened by the salutary effects of a bottle of vintage champagne. I put the 100,000-lira bill on the plate and the waiter didn't bat an eyelash.

Again, however, instead of the change, the manager appeared. He was a very distinguished-looking man, and with sincere anguish told me that he had cashed a check for a customer a short while ago and couldn't give me change. With manorial aloofness, I informed him that it was the only denomination I had. The manager sweetly begged me to be patient for a few minutes.

I sat quietly for a quarter of an hour and then was invited to enter the manager's office. There I found the manager and a less distinguished-looking man, who proved to be an officer of the peace. He waved my dearly beloved 100,000-lira note under my mustache.

"Yours?" he barked.

"Yes," I answered.

"I'm so glad you recognize it," he said nastily. "Even if you had said no, it would have been a useless waste of time. The owner of the restaurant where you scrounged a meal this noon took down the serial number. It's the same bill."

"I didn't scrounge a meal," I answered. "I left him a perfectly good check!"

"Precisely," the man laughed sarcastically. "A 'perfectly good check' which can't be processed till Monday, because today is Saturday. So now how are we going to straighten things out?"

"Very simple," I said. "The manager here gives me my change and I go on my way. Unless you've been able to prove this bill is counterfeit, of course."

"I never said any such thing!"

"Then, everything's in order. This is a banknote of the Italian Republic, and in Italy it's against the law to refuse to accept it."

"Quite right," the manager said, "but the law goes on to say, 'unless I don't have change for it.' "

"I couldn't care less whether you do or not, at this point. You accept my 100,000-lira note and give me in return only 10,000 lire to get home on. Then Monday, when you have a chance to make change for it at the bank, you can send me the rest. Here's my driver's license and other identification. Take down all the information you need."

I took my license out of my wallet and handed it to the manager. Inside the fold of the license a piece of paper was wadded. I had completely forgotten about it. It was a banknote of 1,000 Swiss francs that I'd changed some days before for a Swiss friend of mine and that I'd intended to bring to the bank. The manager unfolded the Swiss note and then asked me: "Excuse me, but why didn't you pay with this?"

"Apart from the fact that I didn't remember having it in my pocket," I explained, "why should I pay with a banknote worth 142,000 lire if you don't have change for 100,000 lire? Anyway, if you'll take it, go ahead."

The manager opened a drawer in his desk and handed over 124,000 lire on the button.

"I see, you were only pretending not to have change," I said, thoroughly irritated now.

"And you tried to foist off that worthless piece of paper on me, so we're even," he said.

"I didn't try to foist anything off on you!" I protested. "That 100,000 note of mine is perfectly good! I . . ."

"That's enough!" the officer of the peace shouted. "Nobody's said anything about counterfeit money! You keep your mouth shut and run along home. And try not to be such a wise guy!"

I filed away the 100,000 note in my wallet, collected my car, and started home. I've thought about that trip often, but I still don't understand what it was all about.

My House

✦

Hey," said Jo, "did you go through the First World War?"

"I certainly did," I answered. "I can still taste the disgusting flavor of the bread, which molded before it ever reached the pantry, and the watered-down milk which was sweetened with salt. And the lines we formed to get two drops of rancid olive oil and a chunk of sour lard on the ration coupons. Luckily a relative of ours belonged to the cavalry division stationed in our city, and once in a while he would come to see us and bring me a few pocketsful of oats stolen from the horses."

Jo cut me short. "What you're talking about isn't war. War is what my grandfather went through, standing in the mud of the trenches for months on end, full of lice, freezing and starving to death, under storms of bombs and poisonous gases."

"Jo," I explained, "on the 24th of May 1915, I was seven years and twenty-three days old. I couldn't fight in the war the way your grandfather did."

"Too bad," she said. "Because the Government is giving

the neediest veterans of World War I a pension of 70,000 lire a year and to all veterans alike, a gold metal."

"Plus a magnifying glass to see the gold medal with," Margherita answered, chuckling.

I must say that this sort of humor is not to my liking. People who are always complaining about the insensitivity, indifference, and stinginess of the Government bore me. I've read about government or municipal employees who are sent into retirement with an honorarium of 130 million lire and a pension of 800,000 lire a month. I know about the law passed on January 4, 1968, to relocate persons displaced by the earthquake of 1915 in Abruzzi. Now what about this veterans' pension?

Let's be fair: What exactly did a soldier do in World War I? After all, he made war, which is a filthy business condemned even by professional military men. What he did was this: waste his time taking potshots at the enemy, plotting ambushes, making little excursions into the mountains, and so forth. Why should the Government consider him in the same context as the diligent functionary who for years and years has traced out his firm and responsible signature at the foot of vitally important documents, thereby giving a fair salary to thousands of deserving workers? And, as far as the relocation of persons displaced by the earthquake of 1915 in Abruzzi—isn't it inspiring how the Government never fails to take into account its sacred obligations? I challenge you to find me a person who would come to your house and say to you, "Now boy, fifty-three years ago I promised you a job. It's your turn now: here's a fine job as an office boy." The Government does everything it's supposed to do. But since the things that the Government is supposed to do are endless in number, it's only right that everyone should wait in good faith, because the Government, if it will not allow the citizen to neglect his duties toward it, will certainly not permit the citizen to renounce a single one of his rights derived from it.

I made the above speech to Margherita, and she laughed and shrugged her shoulders. "Imagine that!" she said.

"I frown on this skepticism of yours," I chided her. "In any case, you will soon have proof that I'm right. In fact, it's today that they're coming to check the new wing I've built onto the house to verify my being able to enjoy the benefits awarded by the Government for constructing a building not in the luxury category. The man who allows himself the luxury of building luxuriously should pay for it; it's only fair."

Accompanied by a young man with a notepad and various tools, the government functionary arrived. I led them toward the new wing, and the young man, obeying a sign from the functionary, began to check whether the building followed the blueprint I had presented to the Office of Housing and Construction, along with five pounds of forms and declarations. He measured the exterior perimeter, the height, and the thickness of the walls. Everything agreed with the plan.

"What about the foundations?" the functionary barked.

"They're underneath," I answered stupidly.

"I see!" said the functionary. "You presume to tell a licensed architect that the foundations 'are underneath.' You have indicated here a foundation made of certain materials and of certain dimensions. How can I check it if you've already built a sumptuous sidewalk which hinders us from digging the necessary holes to make our tests?"

I shrugged. "I don't believe there is such a thing as common foundations and luxury foundations, sir."

"This is for me to judge!" the functionary said brusquely. Then he looked at the rustic wall and tested it with his knuckles. "Exposed brick wall," he snorted. "While everybody uses prefabricated concrete blocks, here we have genuine terracotta brick, just like the great feudal lords used to build their sumptuous palaces! Luxury. Mark it down."

He looked up at the eaves and his eyes opened wide. "Your gutters," he whinnied. "They're a strange reddish color. What are they made of?"

"Copper," I answered.

"*Copper?*" he howled, "Why didn't you have them made of silver instead?"

I explained that zinc-plated gutters don't weather well. Copper costs more but it lasts indefinitely, which in the long run makes it more economical. He laughed wickedly while the assistant wrote feverishly in his notebook. Then he stopped short in front of the door to the courtyard.

"Well well well! What have we here? A precious marble threshold, like some kind of Greek temple!"

"One single piece of marble of the commonest sort measuring two by thirty by ninety centimeters."

He retorted that 5,400 cubic centimeters of marble are a luxury. Then he rapped on the wood of the door and inquired, "Teak, rosewood, or pitchpine?"

"None of them," I answered. "Common fir, stained and varnished."

"Yes! But stained by De Chirico and varnished by

Picasso!" Margherita's perfidious voice qualified. "The key-hole, however, was carved by Lucio Fontana. Perhaps, being an architect, you will be able to detect his characteristic treatment of small round spaces."

The functionary whirled around and flashed a vicious look at Margherita, who had crept up behind us. In turning, he noticed the metallic meshing (made of zinc-covered iron wire) which fences off our vegetable garden, and he asked acidly if it was made of calibrated stainless steel wire.

We stepped inside the door varnished by Picasso and found ourselves in a rustic hall with whitewashed walls. The floor was covered with wheat, oats, potatoes, and onions.

"Majestic!" he exclaimed. "You use it for receptions, I imagine."

"Not at all. For storing wheat, grain, potatoes, etc."

"Oh, I almost forgot you are a farmer!" he said ironically. "Jot this down, Salvatore. Ground floor: luxurious reception room. Where's the staircase to the upper floors?"

"There isn't one," I answered. "We use the staircase in the old house. The granary is isolated from the rest of the building."

We climbed to the "upper floors" (which are one floor with two rooms and facilities) and here the functionary decided that the electric fixtures, consisting of a frosted glass bowl in the center of each ceiling that can be turned on or off from two switches (actually three, in the corridor!), were "science-fictional" and "contemporary Sybaritic," which Salvatore dutifully jotted down.

Inside the bathroom he lost his temper. "Artistic revet-ments preciously decorated, marbles, superfine porcelain, non-standard faucets (silver plate?), etched mirrors, extravagant fixtures which produce graduated water temperature ranging from hot to cold in mixture," he dictated excitedly. "How dare you describe this as a bathroom! The Baths of Caracalla is what this is!"

Going downstairs again, I heard him speaking to his assistant not of luxury but of ostentation and offending the poor. Once in the courtyard our dog Ful came bounding in and took to careening around the legs of the functionary, barking madly. The functionary stopped dead, with a worried look on his face. I introduced Ful. "He's a dratahar. It's a rare breed obtained from crossing—"

"—the Aga Khan with the Great Khan of the Tartars!" Margherita broke in. "The most luxurious crossbreed in the world. Watch out because he's only fed caviar, which makes him hungry, hence dangerous. We used to keep him muzzled and on a chain. But since his muzzle was platinum and his chain solid gold, they were stolen."

The functionary moved off, backward so as not to lose sight of Ful. We went inside and Margherita said to me: "Giovanni, fortunately the man didn't hear your speech glorifying the Government. Otherwise he would have pronounced you a deluxe idiot."

I told her that was an absurd assumption to make. In fact, all you have to do is look at my face and you know I'm only a common idiot.

Vacation My Way

☼

I need a bit of vacation," I said after mature reflection.

Jo, never one to miss a trick, asked sarcastically, "A bit of vacation after two months at the shore?"

According to Jo I must be a man perennially on vacation because I spend part of the year working in the country, part in the mountains, and part at the shore. And to tell the truth, it's at the shore that my vacation becomes least vacation-like. In fact, from my little study in the country I can see a fair piece of the plains, and from my little study in the mountains I can see a lot of mountains, but at the shore all I can see is the tops of a lot of trees bounded off by a row of houses. They tell me that beyond the houses the sea begins. I have yet to see it, but the people who inform me of this interesting phenomenon are quite respectable, so I take it on faith.

This being the case, after many years of "working vacations" I felt the need of a bit of playing vacation.

Let me take a giant step into the past and explain that among the memories of my very distant happy childhood, first place goes to my grandmother Giuseppina's house. It's a marvelous house, something out of the fairy tales: square, squat, yellow with green shutters. No modern architect could ever succeed in creating a house as lovely, comfortable and rational—a great vaulted vestibule on the ground floor, with the kitchen and breakfast room to one side, and the pantry, stairs and library on the other. On the first floor, the same layout: vestibule, three large bedrooms, the large room containing wooden wardrobes, and the stairway leading to the granary, which has an airy, high ceiling, and oval windows.

At the ends of the ground-floor vestibule, there are two large doors with glassed-in porches. One at the north facing the tree-lined drive that leads to the gravel road carrying you across several kilometers of the property to a battered old country road. The south door opens on a courtyard; there is a jasmine tree trained around one side of the porch, and around the other a rosemary bush.

Across the courtyard there is a shack containing the wood pile, the well, the laundry with its stove, and a workroom. Opposite the shack there's a stable for the horse and a shed for the carriage. The fourth side of the courtyard is closed off by a large arbor of muscatel grapes. If you go through the arbor you'll see a field of medicinal herbs and grapevines that runs down to the banks of the river.

Surrounding the house there are shaggy old trees and a vast, untamed hedge that hides the sharecropper's cottage, stable, and workshed.

Inside my grandmother's house are buried the best days of my life. Every summer, when school was over, I went to spend the holidays with my grandmother Giuseppina. The moment I arrived I took off my shoes and didn't put them back on till I went home to begin school again.

When grandmother Giuseppina died she left the house to one of my mother's sisters, who in turn left it to her son. This cousin of mine had kept the house exactly as it had been and lived there with his family until his children finally dragged him off to the city. Before leaving the old house he had written me: "Why don't you come here and take a little holiday? You'll find the house unchanged from the time when you spent summers here. It grieves my heart to think of its being abandoned by everybody . . ."

So we went there, and passing between the high hedges of the country lane, I experienced the immense joy of touring through a glory of dust, making pebbles skitter right and left. I found the house exactly as I had remembered it. The plants were older and more unruly, the yellow paint had gone a bit white. But then, so had I.

Inside, everything was in perfect order. The old share-cropper's wife was a good caretaker and treated everything with love and respect.

The minute she was inside the door, Jo gave a shriek. "There's no light!"

"That's right," I explained. "No electricity, therefore no motors, no icebox, no vacuum cleaner, no washing machine, no TV, no boiler. The only machine is a bottle-opener, which you will find hanging on the kitchen wall. No gas, but a wood-burning stove. No running water, but beside the sink a hook on which hangs a bucket. You make light by lighting up a kerosene lamp or a candle."

Jo went upstairs to explore the first floor and came down

immediately, whimpering. "The bathroom!" she squeaked. "Where's the bathroom?"

"There is a bathroom," I said. "You take baths in the laundry. There's a pump from the well, a stove to heat the water, and a nice poplar-wood tub. Right next to it is the outhouse."

"And if you have to go at night . . ." she babbled.

"The same as during the day. You come down the stairs, you leave the house, and you walk over to the outhouse."

Jo turned to Margherita, horrified. "Mrs. Guareschi, why aren't you saying anything?"

Margherita shrugged her shoulders. "The fact is, Jo, when I was little I lived in a house much worse than this because we lived in the city. Still, I don't think your own house . . ."

"That doesn't make any difference!" Jo cut in. "Once you've achieved prosperity, why should you give it up? You don't take steps backwards!"

"Jo," I said softly, "you're convinced that Prosperity is made up of electrical appliances, central heating, TV, and so on. In reality you're simply at the mercy of an overpowering number of motors and mechanisms and all you need is a power failure for your entire household to fall apart. Here nothing can fall apart, no strike can affect the running of your household. Believe me, you need a holiday too. Progress makes you into a slave, and here one is free."

"Here we return to the age of cavemen!" Jo retorted. "What do you do at night if you don't have a TV or even a transistor radio?"

"You listen to the crickets and the frogs and the nightingales. Apart from everything else, they sing better than your Rock idols. If you don't like their music, the most classical in the world, then you can entertain yourself with your own thoughts."

"Rubbish!" the girl protested. "When the TV's on, I can think and then rethink what I see on TV. Just the way I do when I go to the movies. All by myself, what am I going to think?"

"Jo, wouldn't you like to become different people, live through this or that adventure?"

"Sure, but without TV and the movies how can I think about people I'd like to be or things I'd like to do? TV is the railroad to fantasy, after all."

"Perhaps, but a railroad that takes you where *it* wants to go. And it's no sure thing that the destination is worthwhile. You should think for yourself."

"Too tiring," Jo concluded.

We ate by the light of the kerosene lamp: a discreet, warm, restful light.

I found stacks of the *Sunday News* from 1899 to 1922; they made fascinating reading. It was so pleasant to be able to read about the things that were happening in the world around the time I was born.

I slept soundly and was awakened by a shout from Jo: "Smell it! Smell it!" I ran to the window. It was a fresh, clean morning filled with sunlight, and after so many years I smelled again the perfume of baking bread. I put some homely old clothes on and ran over to the sharecropper's house to watch them take the fresh bread out of the oven.

"We're the only people left in the neighborhood who make our bread at home," the sharecropper's old wife explained to me.

Even Jo had come down to watch the miracle of the bread from up close. Then Margherita came in.

I had put on my slippers, but I threw them off and found my feet again bare against the earth. The sensation lifted half a century off my shoulders. Then I filled a pail from the well pump and, with a fat hunk of bread tucked under my arm I went to look for the row of early grapes. I found it and as in the past picked the golden grapes, cleaned them, and threw them into the pail to remove the stems, the way my grandmother Giuseppina taught me to.

Fresh bread and grapes: a fabulous breakfast. I also found a peach tree, covered with fruit—the ugly kind that nobody seems to know tastes best.

From the distant house, a voice called to me.

"Coming, grandma!" I answered.

"Have you washed?"

"Yes, grandma," I lied shamelessly. "Even my neck and ears."

I walked as far as the river bank. From there, I would have whistled downstream and Gigi would have answered my whistle.

I stuck my fingers in my mouth and whistled. But Gigi didn't answer that time. Instead, I saw an old man with a large gray mustache appear on the road leading to the house hidden behind the bank of acacias. When he was closer to the bank I recognized him: it was Gigi's father. Just the same as he had been those many, many years ago. After a bit of huffing and puffing he climbed up the river bank and planted himself in front of me. "Giovanni," he said breathlessly. "I heard you, but I didn't whistle back because I can't waste my breath any more. Everybody has his own problems."

"Yours are much smaller than mine," I wanted to answer, "because you don't feel the need to come into my world, but I want to move into yours."

We had a long chat sitting on the bank of the river. Then I went back to the old house and wandered through it inch by inch, rediscovering thoughts and dreams that I had believed were lost.

That night, at dinner, Margherita said, "Yes, Giovanni, everything else can go, but I think we should at least have a telephone. Just think, if one suddenly got ill . . ."

"But on the other hand, if one suddenly got well," Jo answered, "what would be the point of a telephone?"

A subtle observation that was strictly logical, and Margherita said, "This is true too."

The Importance of Being Massimo

"M*assimo!*"

Inevitably at Italian seaside resorts there is a woman with a child named Massimo. The woman has a harsh, authoritarian, shrill, disagreeable voice which can be heard over all the rest, and it seems as if the woman's unique function is to persecute her unfortunate child.

"Massimo, don't run! Massimo, don't jump! Massimo, don't drink that! Massimo, don't eat that! Massimo, don't breathe!" (To tell the truth, I've actually never heard that last phrase, but I've always expected to hear it.)

Don't misunderstand me. I don't mean to make generalizations. That is, I don't mean to say that the above happens at all Italian seaside resorts. I'm only saying that, as long as I've been going to beaches, every summer it happens that I hear this petulant, imperious voice. The people are not always the same; each year we have a different woman and a different Massimo. Which makes this phenomenon all the more interesting and leads one to think that the word "Massimo," given its tonic accent falling on the first syllable, eminently lends itself to being pronounced in an imperious tone of voice.

This year, for example, I spent only a few days at the shore. I preferred to suffocate here in the Valley, where the atmosphere is boiling hot, humid, and fetid. Fetid, because the farmers like to scatter the liquid waste from their stables and pigpens at the hottest time of day and they accomplish this by using high-pressure tanks whose powerful jets atomize the liquid, filling the air with a gas so vile it takes your breath away. Still, for me it's better to suffer such discomforts than face the herds unchained by mass tourism, for whom a vacation seems more like a vendetta.

There's no difference, when you come right down to it, between the Sans-culottes who stormed the royal palaces to shatter statuary and slash paintings, tapestries, priceless furniture, and the tourist rabble of today who destroy peace, silence, poetry, beauty, and any possibility of relaxing and resting, with the clatter of their cars, the shrieking of their transistor radios, the howling of their portable record-players, and their odious children brought up in the school of Rita Pavone and Mad Magazine. This horde invades beaches, forests, and parks, leaving behind piles of waxed paper, orange peels, empty beer cans, and leftover bread and sausage. This horde avenges itself by destroying, contaminating, and polluting everything which up until a short time ago was reserved to the privileged. One still remembers those mournful postwar train rides and the stupendous satisfaction derived by the horde from eating box lunches of fried fish and gulping down Chianti straight from the bottle, with their muddy feet propped up on the red velvet of the seats that were once first-class. What joy they got from leaving cigarette holes in the hateful red velvet, symbol of the privileged classes, and smearing it with oil from sardine tins and even slicing out large swatches with penknives to take home to make into slippers.

The automobile boom and mass tourism have unleashed the horde, and if I detest confusion, the smell and roar of the crowd, still I cannot pretend that 200,000 people ought to give up, just for the sake of my delicate sensibilities, spending their holidays at certain seaside resorts. However, I myself can give up doing so.

Therefore, since this summer seems to be the acme of the touristic boom, I spent only the few days necessary to help Margherita, Jo, and Michelone get themselves settled into my house on the Adriatic Riviera. But in those few days, I discovered that this summer too contained the usual woman with the child named Massimo.

There are houses which are tiny on the outside and enormous inside. Ordinarily a house, for arcane technical reasons, meaning the thickness of walls, is larger on the outside than inside. However, at seaside resorts, you will find minuscule houses which, during the winter months, strain at the seams with three people inside but develop into comfortable quarters for twenty people the minute the season begins. These houses don't have basements or attics or rubber walls, and it's very difficult to grasp how they can accommodate so many people. Do they sleep standing up? Or in layers? Or, as the expression goes, like the seven of spades (three at the head of the bed, three at the foot, and one in the middle)? Don't ask me; but the fact is, somehow they manage. Perhaps using the windows as doors helps out.

And all of us read the newspapers and have seen how Her
Britannic Majesty's extraordinary student population has
cleverly managed to adapt their living-space requirements to
the new dimensions of the British Empire, succeeding in
thrusting themselves forty at a time into phone booths and
Microbuses.

My own shore house has a large terrace facing, shall we
say, the countryside. The "countryside" consists of a vegetable garden that doesn't belong to me and, twenty yards
away, is bounded off by an immense condominium fifteen or
twenty stories tall.

I was sitting on the terrace watching Michelone try to
shear through the front tire of my old bicycle with his tiny
teeth, when suddenly I heard voices coming from a cluster
of houses situated to the south. I gave a start.

"Massimo! Drop that vile mess instantly!"

We were off to the races. The authoritarian lady with the
little boy named Massimo was with us again.

"Massimo, stop reading that trash! Massimo, it's time for
your pill! Massimo, it's time for your drops! Massimo, I've
told you a thousand times that those thrillers get you so
excited you can't sleep!"

This time, Massimo had to be slightly older than his
predecessors, not just because of the thrillers but also because after a while I heard the lady yell, "Massimo, you've
got to stop throwing away money on that damned skeet-
shooting of yours! The same goes for the billiards! Massimo, you're dreadful. I can tell by your breath you've been
smoking! Massimo, you're a moron!"

I forgot to tell you: all this was happening on a stormy
afternoon when there was no point in going to the beach.

This meant the children had to stay locked up indoors, turning them into so many rabid animals.

Night fell, finally.

"Massimo, you're an imbecile! You don't peel potatoes like that! Massimo, don't get distracted or you'll burn my gravy! Massimo, don't squish the cheese in your fingers before you eat it!"

Dinner was ready.

"Massimo, will you please tuck your napkin in! Massimo, you idiot, don't stuff yourself like a goose! Massimo, try not to spill gravy on your shirt as usual! Massimo, don't drink so much, liquids dilute the digestive juices! Massimo, you filthy pig, don't dip your bread in the gravy! Massimo, peel your fruit like a decently brought-up person, with a knife and fork! Massimo, wipe your mouth off!"

Dinner was over.

"Massimo, you worthless goldbrick, nothing doing! If you haven't washed and dried the dishes, you can't go out for an icecream! Massimo . . . !" At that moment an infernal crash of dishes and glasses shattering broke the night air. I waited in vain for the acidulous, imperious voice to make some comment.

Instead I saw, shortly afterward, a little man about forty years old come out of the house with an umbrella and a suitcase. In passing he exchanged a few words with the man next door, who was hanging out of the window. "Are you going away, Signor Massimo?"

"I'm going back to the city."

"All by yourself?"

"All by myself."

"Have a good vacation, Signor Massimo."

From our kitchen Margherita and Jo had followed the whole fracas too. "If you want my opinion," Jo said, "he killed her by smashing her head in with the dishes, soup tureen, and glasses. Then he quickly chopped her up into pieces, and now he's carrying away, in that suitcase, the larger pieces of his wife to keep some insane surgeon from sewing them together again. You'll see, the whole story will be in the papers tomorrow."

"I don't agree with the macabre details about the pieces of the wife inside the suitcase, but clearly he's killed her," Margherita answered.

Just then, the high, shrill, imperious voice floated through the darkness. "Massimo, watch that you don't forget your umbrella in the taxi the way you always do!"

Massimo was already halfway down the street. Passing a trash can, he stopped, lifted the lid, snapped the umbrella in two over his knee, and threw the remains into the can. Then he went on his way.

A virile act, to be sure; but still, she had had the last word.

"How many years do you think he would have gotten for killing his wife?" Jo asked me.

"I think the standard sentence is twenty years," I said.

"He'd have been better off killing her," Jo declared.

Margherita added, "I thought this type of wife only existed in England or America. But how can a man marry a witch like that?"

"Wives wouldn't be witches if their husbands weren't fools," Jo said without hesitation.

From outside we heard an explosion, but it wasn't the tragic end of the noisy fracas. Michelone had managed to gnaw through the front tire of my old bicycle with his tiny teeth. Margherita dashed outside. "Stop him! He might eat the valve along with the tire!" she shouted imperiously.

The Builder

✧

Once upon a time, at least here where we live, houses had thick walls and small windows. The walls were made of solid brick, and before the heat managed to penetrate their thickness of two or three feet summer was over.

Then Progress and the building industry invented construction blocks made of a series of holes held together by a minimal amount of clay or concrete, the ratio of holes to clay or concrete being about six to one. Progress and hygiene (how many vile messes have been perpetrated in your name, O Hygiene!) widened windows, covering them with charming plastic shades. Now people die of the heat in the summertime.

To compensate, air conditioning became necessary, which is only reasonable in a consumer-oriented civilization whose principal goal is the creation of new needs and, therefore, new industries. Prosperity is the syndrome by which mankind destroys forests and parks in order to replace them with electric utilities that dehumidify and purify the air, by which mankind grows fresh vegetables for the sole purpose of freezing or canning them.

When I was a boy, in my part of the country there were

water holes, canals, and streams. But the countryside was improved by removing all the water; to compensate— thanks to vast land reclamation projects involving an ingenious and astronomically expensive network of artificial irrigation facilities, and thanks to the decimation of the forests, when the sky buckets down rain and the mountain snow unexpectedly melts—the water cascades onto the plain with an unheard-of swiftness and violence, inundating towns and cities. Still, there's no water today. Wells beneath houses have gone dry; millions of pumps are lowering the water level and siphoning it off to factories which restore it to the land irrevocably polluted and unusable. The farmers irrigate the land artificially even when it's raining, just as automobiles are used to get from one's house to one's garage.

But even in the fields the water is polluted, since the land is saturated with chemical fertilizers. It's the era of legal poisons, and the brassy newspaper campaigns against the "sophistication" of foodstuffs seems all the more ridiculous in a world in which every year fruit trees undergo thirty or forty "treatments" of insecticides and other terrifying poisons, a world in which one is permitted to poison indiscriminately the air, the earth, the water, vegetables, citrus and other fruit trees, and, with the metal staples that have taken the place of thread and stitching, one's very shoes.

The time isn't far off when we will have to consider supplying soda-pop bottles and wine flasks with filters, the way we've already done with cigarettes. I don't know how they will make filters for bread, steaks, chicken, cheese, and eggs; but dieticians are very clever and surely they'll be able to cope.

In my rather long life I've been hot but never as hot as

now. This heat too is dirty, and saturated with poisons. It's exactly like this famous "Prosperity," which is two parts loud noise, one part carcinogenic synthetic dyes, one part publicity, one part stench and toxic gases, all the ingredients of effective progress.

This new Prosperity makes an entire apartment out of one room Old Style. "Night area" is the term for the spacelet in which one manages to sleep only after having ingested a handful of sleeping pills, and "day area" is the closet in which frozen food is eaten, in which Sandra Milo is the subject of conversation, in which young people grow senile before television sets. In combination, "night area" and "day area" give the pleasant sensation of spaciousness. ("This is your day area," says a voluptuous model with a seductive voice, pointing to an armchair arranged in a room six feet wide and five feet long. "And this is your night area," she says, giving the armchair a whack that converts it into a cot three feet wide and six feet long.)

This new Prosperity invented mass tourism, which actually is anti-tourism and anti-prosperity since it causes the subject to wedge his automobile, the result of the "economic miracle," into an endless line of cars solely for the pleasure of sitting behind a steering wheel in a cloud of poisonous gases, eyes riveted on the bumper of the car ahead.

This new Prosperity, to which we owe our highways with their high-sounding names, highways that are supposed to cut the fatigue of a journey in half with the singular result that the herd of motorists travels 600 kilometers on a weekend instead of 300. An orgy of misspent kilometers, of sweat, of vicious quarrels that transform a weekend into a chamber of horrors, a searing of nerve-ends, the motto of the "economic miracle" being, "If it's not confusing and deafening, then it's not entertainment."

Milan was so pretty before the economic miracle. We used to spend our summer vacations in a nice spot in Piemonte, and when the August vacationers descended on Piemonte, Margherita and I climbed into the car and spent the month of August in Milan, deliciously deserted and quiet, drinking its flavorsome water and avoiding the depredations of foreign tourists dumped like sacks of potatoes into the middle of the Piazza del Duomo from travel agencies' buses.

But that Milan is long gone and irretrievable, submerged under a mist of toxic vapors and water shortages. And all the roads leading there are packed with people maddened by the heat and running foolishly toward places where it's hotter still.

Don't worry, I'm getting to the story now. It was a sweltering hot August day. Where could I go for a bit of peace and fresh air?

The only answer was to go beyond Cortina, to the springs at Bacedasco. I arrived in Cortina, left the car in the huge parking lot, and as I was locking the door, an obese, important-looking gentleman pulled up in his Alfa Romeo with a Milan license plate.

"Is this it?" he asked, looking around disappointedly.

"No," I said, "the valley with the hot springs can't be seen from here. It's a kilometer away. You buy a ticket over at that booth and then a little train takes you there."

"A little train!" the important gentleman snorted. "What is this, Toyland? Do you mean to tell me they haven't been able to build a road one kilometer long out here?"

"There's a road," I explained. "But you can only go on

foot or on horseback. They don't want cars up there. Apart from the ten hot springs and the mud baths, the most important thing about the place is that you can move around calmly without having to listen to the racket and smell the stench of cars."

The little train arrived and we got on.

"This is insane!" the important gentleman exclaimed. "In the age of automobiles here we are leaving them behind and taking this infantile train! They can't be serious!"

"The fact is, this is one of the few places where they *are* serious; they have a healthy respect for nature and, therefore, for humanity."

He growled something about having to converse with cave dwellers and I realized that my companion was one of that special breed of Milanese "progressives" whose "progressivism" reduces itself to allocating vast funds to murder Italy. The sort who have ruined the Ligurian Riviera, Cervinia, and other spectacularly beautiful places with their real-estate speculations; the sort who, left to their own devices, would convert Portofino into a Coney Island of the Mediterranean overnight and tear down the Ca' d'Oro in Venice to put up a skyscraper like the Empire State Building. These Milanese have built skyscrapers in their own city and repulsive barracks they call condominiums all along the Adriatic Riviera; having accomplished that, they float around Italy followed by cortèges of trucks filled with cement, I-beams, and all manner of construction equipment.

We arrived in the fresh, stunningly beautiful little valley, into the basin of which the ten hot springs spout, giving the goodness of their waters to all comers. The important gentleman lost control and started babbling about having to begin building thermal establishments, hotels, restaurants, and nightclubs immediately. His eyes sparkled, he envisioned steam shovels, cement mixers, Caterpillars crawling all over the forested hillsides, regurgitating clean white cement to cover the mountain and make it useful. When he discovered that certain of the boulders were outcroppings of fossil conglomerates more than 35 million years old, his eyes popped. And when I told him the story of a dog infected with mange (this was at the time of the search for the springs) who had come many hundreds of kilometers just to bathe in one of the hot springs which turned out to be a cure for all manner of dermatological ailments, the important man began to tremble with excitement.

"Where is this dog now?" he shouted.

"I don't know," I answered. "What difference does it make?"

"*What difference does it make!* Haven't you any idea what it means to be able to use a dog in a publicity campaign? A poor, proletarian dog, intelligent of course, having no financial resources at all, tries and tries to find the cure for his skin disease, and all by himself discovers the one fountain in the world that is the answer to all his prayers! Picture this: a luscious big hotel with the Hot Spring of the Dog, in front of which stands a monument, a twice-life-size statue of the dog!"

It was nine in the morning and the little valley was steeped in a miraculous freshness. Tiny ponies wandered freely and happily among the plants, and thousands of birds chirped away (it seems impossible, in this day and age, that birds can still chirp). The peacefulness was overpowering. I stretched out in a comfortable deckchair and sipped at an unpretentious glassful of water filtered through fossils 35 million years old, which cost me 35 lire. But that diabolical Milanese gentleman was intent on ruining my day and sat down next to me, determined to sketch out his entire plan for my benefit.

A doctor I know walked by, and I asked him: "Isn't there a spring here that paralyzes constructors and real-estate speculators?"

"Hardly," he said, but the important gentleman rose to his feet indignantly and moved off.

Later, on the road home, he passed me in his Alfa Romeo and I had a pleasant thought. But, sad to say, the Alfa squealed round the curve without smashing itself against the huge Caterpillar creeping up in the opposite lane.

Margherita as a Liar

✵

Is the telephone a sign of progress or of regression? Is it a help to humankind, or does it do damage? It depends: it's a sign of progress when it's we who do the telephoning, it's regression when others ring us up. Personally, I consider the phone in my house a veritable enemy. Even though I know that out of every hundred phone calls I receive at least ninety-nine of them are sure to be useless, if the phone rings, each time I must answer it, because it just might be that one important call in a hundred.

Now let us talk about women.

I don't want to intimate that women are liars. I'm simply saying that women, if they feel like it, are much better liars than men. And by saying this, I don't mean to malign women. Lying is merely a particular way of telling the truth.

Therefore, Margherita being a woman, when I had a phone installed in my house it didn't worry me. "Margherita," I explained, "when people ring up, you answer. Say that I've just gone out. Make them give their name. If it's important I'll call them back."

This plan was a resounding failure because Margherita would stammer and stutter and inevitably wind up saying,

"Oh, here he is right now! Hang on and I'll turn him over."

Margherita found it humiliating to tell lies over the phone, so I tried to help her. "Look, when the phone rings I'll go and stand in the hall. That way it won't be a lie when you say I've gone out." But this system didn't work either, so I simplified it further. Say, "I'm the maid. Mr. Guareschi has gone to Turin. Give me your message and I'll tell him when he returns."

This worked for a while, then Margherita got bored with shipping me off to Turin verbally and tried to make things easier for me by saying I was in certain smaller towns closer to home. One day she said I was in Paullo and got this answer: "Marvelous! I'll ring the Paullo operator. It's a tiny town and I'm bound to find him. How's he dressed?"

I'm not going to give you a line-by-line recitation of the history of a pathetic wretch persecuted by the telephone. All I will say is that when Jo arrived to become our domestic assistant, I thought all my problems were solved. "Jo," I said, "tell anyone that calls I'm out. Write down their names."

Jo didn't argue; she religiously did what she was told. I had the satisfaction of receiving this sort of message: "Some man named Lazzetti or Franchini or Perotta rang up, a name like that. He says he can't wait any longer."

"Wait for what?"

"Don't ask me. I don't meddle in your business affairs."

So one fine day I decided to go to Milan. Milan is the most extraordinary city in the world because you can find the answer to all your problems in Milan. Perhaps you wouldn't believe that, given the fact that in spite of its skyscrapers it seems like an overgrown provincial town. But the truth is, you can find anything in Milan. From narcotics racketeering to a machine for pitting cherries, from gloves with six fingers to laser microscopes. Therefore I went to Milan, found the solution to my problem, and brought it home with me in a cardboard box.

When I had opened the box Margherita gave a sigh of relief. "I see you've had the good sense not to bring a secretary home with you."

"Much better than a secretary," I said. "You put the phone on this base, you take off the receiver and hang it on this gadget. You connect the phone to these two little boxes and plug them into the electric outlet. When the phone rings, a tape-recorded voice answers that Mr. Guareschi is out and asks the caller to leave a message which will be recorded automatically. The fellow talks, the electronic device records. When the fellow hangs up the machine goes off and waits for another call. When it suits you, you flip this switch and listen to all the recorded calls. So if you're home, don't worry about the phone if it rings. The machine will take care of it. But even better, supposing we were to take a trip to Bologna for a week—"

"Bologna!" Margherita exclaimed. "A week in the most deplorable city in Europe, which has traffic jams that remind one of the October Revolution? Either we go to Assisi, or we don't go anywhere."

"All right, Assisi," I said. "If we were to spend a week in Assisi and our house were empty, the gadget would record all the calls; but to hear them you wouldn't have to wait to come home because the Top Secret mechanism can be used."

"Sounds like a spy adventure," Jo said, fascinated. "It

says here, you dial your phone number, and when the machine answers you blow this whistle into the receiver which activates some cells inside the machine and the recorder plays back everything over the phone. Of course every machine has a different wave-length sensitivity so nobody else can ring up and whistle into your phone. Then when you hang up the machine goes on acting like a secretary-receptionist."

"Too confusing," Margherita said.

"Much less confusing than the least confusing secretary of flesh and bone," I said.

"I think this is the crowning achievement of electrical appliances," Jo said firmly. "It saves you the annoyance of having to answer the phone and take notes after you've said there's nobody home. Who would have thought that science would invent an electronic liar!"

Jo was so enthusiastic that she consented to have her own clear, resonant voice recorded giving the stock phrases: "Hello. Guareschi residence. Who is calling, please? . . . Mr. Guareschi is not at home. This is a recording. Please repeat your message clearly and it will be recorded automatically . . ." Then she ran off to the tobacconist's to ring up and listen to the sound of her own voice.

We all went to Cremona because the Phenomenon needed some air that was a little less foggy, and when we got back I turned on the electronic secretary. It functioned perfectly. After five normal if boring phone calls from friends, we heard an unexpected but friendly man's voice: "I realize I've dialed the wrong number, but since everything's recorded automatically I would like to sing the famous aria

Dalla sua pace." The young man didn't sing badly and we
rather enjoyed listening to him.

Next came a much less pleasant fellow, who took advantage of the automatic recording to read me the first chapter
of a novel he wanted to send for my editorial opinion.
Thoroughly dreadful. After that came a young lady I don't
know. "Mr. Guareschi, since this is going to be recorded
automatically, let me tell you that I think you're a first-born
idiot and wholly unqualified to speak on the subject of
modern music and publish your opinions of it in the papers.
Worry about something else, why don't you."

Jo burst out laughing but not for long because the next
recording subjected us to a loud masculine voice. "Okay, Jo,
stuff it! I don't give a hairy damn if that fink you work for
has gone to hell in a handbasket. What I'm interested in is
you and I'm telling you, you're not going to get away with
hiding inside that house. I've got my eye on you and if you
turn up at the discothèque next week and drop me in the
middle of a dance again, I'll show you who Gigino is! Oh, so
you don't want to talk! That's good, I like to hear you
listening. Watch it, because if you hang up on me I won't
forget it in a hurry. You better get it through your thick
skull that I'm not used to being dumped on by girls. Now,
just consider yourself lucky I like you. So listen, you partridge, come down out of your pear tree, or I'll pull you
down myself! Bye-bye, ba-bee . . ."

"Isn't that sweet," Margherita commented. "Did you
hear? He calls her a partridge and is asking her to come
down from her pear tree. He must be a sentimental orni-
thologist."

Wednesday night after dinner, Jo went out and came back very soon, extremely agitated.

"Did you come down from your pear tree?" Margherita inquired.

"No, I chased him up a bramble bush. In any case, that machine is a big mistake. When a cretin like that calls it ought to cut him off."

"You're asking too much, ba-bee," Margherita answered, very sweetly. Jo shot a disintegrating look at her.

Out for a Drive
with the Family

I was living in Parma, in a room on the top floor of a shabby house on Borgo del Gesso. I should say, in *the* room on the top floor, because the house consisted of a room on the ground floor, one on the first, one on the second, and mine on the third. An extremely narrow staircase allowed one to get to the upper floors, while the ground floor was easily reached from the street because it was a store where horsemeat was sold. My room was an attic with a ceiling of small beams supported by a huge rafter on which I had printed in large letters: DON'T LOSE YOUR TEMPER.

This was because every time I came into or left the room, inevitably I'd smack my head on the rafter. But I would read the sage admonition and instead of getting angry I would put a damp piece of cloth on my forehead and smile.

Not a sweet smile like Mona Lisa's but, if somewhat forced, still a smile.

I learned many important things while living in that attic. Some I was bound to forget, but never self-control!

The house I own today has large oak rafters with razor-

sharp edges, but I haven't written on them DON'T LOSE
YOUR TEMPER. And nobody's ever heard me cursing
them for bumping my head against them. This might have
something to do with the fact that they're nine and a half
feet from the floor, while the Borgo del Gesso rafters were
five feet from the floor; however, this isn't an issue of inches
but one of principles.

I know how to control myself: that's what I'm trying to
say.

The trouble is that my wife, Margherita, is really two
women. Two women so different from each other that from
time to time she makes me feel like a bigamist. This is the
worst risk involved in marriage. A man in all good faith
believes he's married one woman and suddenly finds two
living with him. Or even three, or none at all.

This being the case, while my self-control is perfect when
I'm dealing with Margherita Number One, the situation
changes radically when I have to cope with Margherita
Number Two.

Margherita Number One is a calm woman who waits
patiently for my return from a concentration camp or jail,
who comes straightaway to fetch me out of the clutches of
the political police and never says another word about these
boring episodes. Margherita Number Two is a panther who
all of a sudden breaks out of her cage and, roaring like a
demon, demands to know at 5:30 P.M., May 16, 1967, with
whom I spent the night on July 5, 1935; since thirty-two
years have gone by and I can't remember, she concludes
menacingly that one day, when she finds out, certain things
which would make your hair stand on end will happen to me.

Margherita Number One is a gentle woman who makes no

demands and is ashamed to go to the bank to cash a certified check, for fear of imposing on the teller's time. Margherita Number Two is an authoritarian woman, one of those who understand and foresee everything; when they talk to you, it's not talking but an accusation, and they explain how you've always been wrong, how you've let yourself be led into messes by everybody, and how in spite of the million opportunities shamelessly put in your path by Fortune, you've never been able to accomplish one tangible thing.

Which is the real Margherita, Number One or Number Two?

Margherita is not a woman of profound culture like Claudia Cardinale, to whom a wife must be at least 12 (twelve) different women (and, of the twelve, bear in mind that one went to an audience with the Pope in a miniskirt—a fact that leads us to consider the possibilities of the other eleven with something less than optimism). Margherita is a simple woman and her change of personality doesn't depend on complicated processes of reasoning. Margherita falls into her second personality the way some poor fellow walking down the street slips on a banana peel.

But fortunately, as I said, I have perfect self-control.

They were a majority and decided that I was going to drive them in the station wagon to some friends of ours who live in Pontenovo. Margherita sat next to me, and the ex-Passionaria, Michelone, and Jo sat in the back seat, and behind them was a basket of things to change Michelone into.

The sunny streets were deserted: Prosperity's hordes

were enjoying their long holiday at the beach. It was a dream to travel at that time of year.

"Don't smoke while you're driving!" Margherita ordered tartly.

"I'm not smoking," I answered sweetly.

"I can see that for myself," she snapped, "but you were thinking about lighting a cigarette. Whenever you're plotting something stupid I can read it in your eyes."

"I don't see how you can read it in my eyes," I said, "since all you can see is my right eye, in profile."

"I can read your eyes even in the dark!" Then she added: "You may remember the time I lit a cigarette for you and you promptly dropped it in your lap."

It was an old story but strictly true and the audience laughed appreciatively.

"Watch out!" exclaimed Margherita. "A car could come out of that street on your right!"

"Nothing's going to come out of the street on the right, because it's not a street at all but a gravel quarry," I shouted.

A tractor stuck its nose out of the little bridge leading to a threshing floor on the left, but I had time to miss him. "Instead of wasting time handing out tickets to people who park in the wrong places," Margherita decided, "the police would do better taking licenses away from senile old men who can't see any more and drive like maniacs!"

I know how to control myself and didn't answer. But shortly before we drove into Solana, a fearsome smell made itself at home in the car.

"Do something about Michelone!" I yelled.

"What do you mean, Michelone!" Passionaria retorted resentfully. "That's the handbrake burning."

I stopped the car, tested the brake, and found it pulled almost all the way up. I let it down again and opened all the windows and vents to get rid of the smell.

"When one seats oneself behind the wheel of a car," Jo said, "one first checks to make sure the handbrake is off."

"I checked!" I shouted. "The handbrake *was* off!"

Margherita stepped in. "Finding myself sitting beside a senile old man who drives like a criminal, naturally I pulled up the handbrake to keep him from going so fast he would kill us all."

"Margherita," I said holding up a fat screwdriver I kept under the driver's seat, "do you remember the screwdriver murder in the papers a few months ago? Well then, you have some money, get out and don't say a word and crawl there on your own steam. You're in town and you can damn well find yourself a taxi."

Margherita got down without a word and clearly had gone back to being Margherita Number One.

I started up the car again, and almost immediately Passionaria explained to me that to take the shortcut, I would have to drive as far as the grist mill rather than turn right after the little church.

It's a big mistake to force a pilot to take a route that he doesn't know. I found myself successively in a large farmyard, then on the drive leading to a cemetery, and then in a small square where dozens of farm trucks loaded with crates of tomatoes were waiting for their turn to make delivery to the cannery.

We were in Fontana, and as soon as we reached the main

square I ordered Passionaria to get out and find her way to our friends' house however she could. Every town has its own taxi service.

Michelone was sleeping soundly in Jo's powerful arms. Once rid of Margherita's daughter we began the march again. But the minute we hit the next village, there we were again with the vile stench that took one's breath away. "That damn handbrake again!" I screamed in exasperation.

"No, this time it's Michelone," Jo answered.

I stopped the car and got out. "Fix him up," I said, handing Jo the car keys. "Then you drive. I'm walking the rest of the way."

"If I were your wife or your daugher I would already have killed you," the girl said, snatching the keys away ungraciously. "You're impossible. There are times when you seem like another man."

"Evidently when Margherita and I got married we thought there were two of us but actually there were four."

"What are you trying to say?"

"It's too complicated to explain. Anyhow, clean up Michelone and get lost."

"Just a minute now!" the girl exclaimed. "I'm here in the capacity of domestic assistant, not as baby-sitter or dry nurse. I'm not hired to keep this tiny walking dungheap clean."

"Oh me," I sighed. "There are even two Jos. Well then, drag him over there where it says 'Dry Cleaners' and get them to dry-clean him."

She started up the car and roared off.

I trudged ahead on foot and when I got to town, sat out under the awning of a restaurant specializing in Lambrusco wine and roast rack of lamb. The restaurant faced the street, and in a short while I saw the station wagon roll up. Passionaria was driving and when she saw me she stopped the car.

"Pappa," Michelone's wicked mother said, pointing to Margherita, "I don't know what's wrong with her today. I'm not driving any more. I'm going to walk the rest of the way with you. She managed to turn poor Jo into a raving maniac too and she won't drive any more."

Passionaria and Jo got out with Michelone, who was all clean again.

Now I fervently hoped that yet a third Margherita would develop, complete with driver's license and capable of shooting off like a rocket and leaving us behind in a cloud of dust.

But there was no Margherita Number Three. Therefore Margherita Number Two clambered grimly out of the station wagon. After a decent treatment of roast rack of lamb and Lambrusco, though, she disappeared, and in her place we had the pleasure of the company of Margherita Number One.

Which goes to show how complicated we all are.

What Makes Michelone Smell like Roses

There are children who, when they cry, gush out tears like squeezed sponges, but the consequences of this phenomenon are only the formation of insignificant puddles on the floor which rarely leak through and form drops on the ceiling of the room below.

Michelone isn't fond of happy mediums and when he cries he sprays tears violently in every direction and as far as six feet away. Barometers have been known to drop when he begins to cry.

I don't want to give the impression that Michelone is one of those loathesome children who cry on the slightest pretext. Of course from time to time he will demolish the corner of a wall knocking his head against it or chip a piece of furniture with his chin—Michelone's not the sort who avoids contact with the hard realities of life. However, rather than bursting into tears he will initiate energetic acts of retaliation. He only cries as an act of protest. But let me make it clear that his protests have nothing in common with the complaints of the long-haired leftists.

Michelone will not put up with any form of tyranny, and the idea of pretending that at a certain moment during the day he should go to bed is the most intolerable of tyrannizations. And he's not wrong, since God did not create all that business called Creation so that men could ignore it sleeping, perhaps escape it by dreaming. Michelone loves Creation precisely the way it is and therefore wants to enjoy it twenty-four hours a day. It's natural that his opinion should clash with the lack of understanding of people who want to subject him to insensitive customs and occasionally try to put him to bed.

Then Michelone cries, and his weeping of protest is so vigorous and virile that his tears bounce against the walls and ceiling.

I'm saying all this to keep you from wondering why the entire neighborhood became alarmed that afternoon hearing the uproar coming from Michelone's room and why Margherita quickly stepped in by ordering Jo to shut Michelone up, if necessary by using brute force.

Jo went upstairs, her eyes filled with grim determination. She came back down ten minutes later, shaking her head. "I'm not qualified to handle this problem," she said as Michelone's shrieks, roars, and shrills continued to shake the very foundations of our house.

"You're not qualified to handle this problem!" Margherita mimicked sarcastically. "I thought child psychology was one of the courses you took to qualify you as a domestic assistant."

"It was," Jo answered. "But this has nothing to do with child psychology. To turn off that monster you're going to have to call a plumber!"

Margherita is a reasonable woman until you bring up the subject of Michelone and the Phenomenon. "Jo, I forbid you to talk about my grandchild as if he were a piece of plumbing! Do you mean to say they didn't teach you *anything* in that family psychology course?"

Jo took in a cubic meter of air and then exploded. "Oh, so we're going to start *that* again, are we! It always comes down to the simple fact that you can't stand the idea of my having some professional pride because I took some courses in domestic science. If your husband can enroll himself in a writer's guild, then why can't I be a member of the domestic assistant's union?"

When you think, apart from other considerations, that too often journalists as hired help are a great deal less free and respectable than servants, Jo had a point. And it's my opinion that the Italian Christian Workers' Association, Housekeeper Division, did splendidly in instituting training courses for domestic servants. Serious courses, with sixteen theoretical areas from balancing the budget to scientific shopping, from alimentation to child-rearing, from etiquette to the culinary arts, from first aid to hygiene, from professional ethics to family psychology. Followed by very difficult examinations consisting of fifty-three tests of practical application.

It is a milestone in the history of society because (as the Italian Christian Workers' Association, Housekeeper Division, points out) "the professional preparation and the transformation of every person employed as a domestic worker into a domestic scientist will be the secret to resolving the crises which often confront Italian families who search in vain for an assistant prepared to solve the problems inherent in the family milieu."

When one considers the fact that in Italy 400,000 women are employed as live-in domestics and another 400,000 as day helpers, one begins to understand the importance of a union for professional domestics.

Margherita does not understand that, Prosperity having reduced the home to a hotel, a professionally trained domestic can keep a family on its feet by taking charge as technical director and spiritual leader. Margherita is convinced that the traditional organization of the family is the only valid one. If a great country whose military tradition runs from Vercingetorix to Napoleon has decided that soldiers should have the right to disobey unjust orders, then one cannot, as Margherita does, ignore the enormous advantages that can be derived by the family from a domestic who refuses to cook harmful foods or to allow disreputable persons inside the house.

The first serious confrontations between Margherita and Jo began when the girl first served beef stroganoff, mushroom bisque, home-made lasagna, veal marsala, steak tartare, and petits-fours iced in two or three different colors, along with other dishes she learned in her cooking course—all elegant foods but impossible for our stomachs to digest. The conflict aggravated itself when Jo pronounced sentence on Michelone and the Phenomenon, saying they were dreadfully brought-up little monsters, just as badly brought up as their parents had been.

Hence, when Margherita heard her beloved grandson referred to as a piece of common plumbing, she lost her temper.

"It obviously irritates you, Mrs. Guareschi," Jo repeated, "that I know a thing or two and have some professional pride."

"Not at all!" Margherita exclaimed. "What infuriates me is that you make us eat food that we can't digest and that you try to make us live according to your rules and not according to our own set ways!"

Jo shook her head. "That's not it at all, and I'm going to write a letter to the union office. In the first place, the training course is all wrong. They should put in a parallel course for employers. It's senseless to train sailors if you're going to give infantry officers command of the ship."

Her analogy was quite apt but it had the effect of lighting Margherita's fuse. "And why should I change over to the navy from the infantry at my age?"

"The destiny of Italy is on the sea!" Jo exclaimed. At that precise instant came the end of the world—something thundered down the stairs and hit the bottom with a horrifying crash.

"It's Michelone!" Margherita screamed.

In one bound Jo reached the foot of the stairs. A few seconds later she was back in the breakfast room. "No, Michelone's still upstairs. What's come down is a cabinet, or, I should say, *was* a cabinet. The little dear dragged it over to the landing and then pushed it down. Maybe he was studying the properties of matter rolling down a flight of stairs to see whether he could do it too."

We ran upstairs and found Michelone fast asleep in the bathtub. Margherita gently picked him up to carry him off to bed. "He sleeps like an angel," she said feelingly. "Smell him, his breath is like roses."

"It ought to be," Jo said disgustedly. "He ate a whole bar of soap."

It was strictly true, but the remark sounded so tactless and indelicate that I couldn't keep myself from a reproof. "Jo," I said, "is this how you use all your good training in family psychology? Would it have hurt you to allow her to keep her illusion that her adorable little grandson smelled like a rose?"

"It's a matter of professional ethics," she answered. "Furthermore, I hope you realize, I didn't say anything about the child's also having eaten half of the bathtub plug."

That act of delicacy truly moved me.

The Ghost of Milan

✧

Milan is an unforgettable city. Like many other persons, one day long ago I too picked up a suitcase, an umbrella, and an insane urge to work, left my small provincial town, and descended on Milan. In a poorly lit office I found myself a table against the wall. I sat down and, after demonstrating to the wall that my head was harder than it was, started to scribble away. Ah, the quantities of fine clean paper I have wasted since that day!

I went back to visit my city as soon as I paid the first two installments on my Millecento.

Milan is an extraordinary city and the only truly alive city in Italy because its dominant element is man. Man as an individual, not the "group" or the "gang." There's nothing in Milan to oppress one with its overwhelming beauty or its fascinating history, not even the Duomo. Since childhood we are accustomed to seeing the Duomo in advertisements and catalogues, inevitably as the background for a bicycle ad, a motorcycle ad, a Panettone Motta ad, and the like. So much so that if one sees a picture of the Duomo by itself it doesn't seem natural: it's naked, removed from its time and environment.

As I was saying, one doesn't forget Milan. Along the asphalt, even the most stunted seedlings brought in from the provincial nurseries sink indestructible roots into the Milanese soil.

War yanked me out of Milan and still today I can see the vicious full moon ogle through the windows of houses gutted by bombs. My house too was disemboweled and my family scattered; but my roots withstood the blast and I returned to Milan at the end of the mess that started in 1941 and at the beginning of the one going on still today. Everything had to be built up from scratch. One had to find a place in the sun again, which was a sore trial because all the places were occupied by people who, having won the war, had taken even my little Millecento in spite of their irreproachable political leanings.

It was a desperate battle fought on the rubble of twenty years, on top of which the people struggled to erect the rubble of the next twenty. The first victory was my Guzzino car, which looked like a stunted red horse hefting on its back a sack of potatoes with a mustache. Then came the Cinquecento, and then the most important conquest of all: a tiny house.

As soon as Margherita had it fixed the way she wanted it, we abandoned it and moved to the country. I had become a part of the house, the most unfortunate part, from morning till night puttering around with hammers, pliers, drills, nails, brooms, vacuum cleaners, and floor polishers. When I wasn't occupied running about the house in a frenzy, I had to sit and listen to Margherita's obsessions with the tremendous, insoluble problems of running a household. I escaped to the country where I'd made a new nest for myself, and there

everything went so well that I had to flee back to my house
in Milan to do my scribbling.

Not even the long sojourn in a distant prison succeeded in
cutting the umbilical cord that linked me to Milan. Once I
paid back my debts and had my car again, I started from
scratch for the third time, and kept on going till I got kicked
out again and sent to another little town.

Now other people live in my house in Milan, but the attic
is still mine and I don't give it up because my sentimental
boat is still moored at the Great Smoggy Dock, which means
that even if my car has a Parma tag my heart has Milan
plates.

In this sad little house there's still the study I had made
for myself and that I would have wanted to fix up so as not
to knock my head against a certain rafter every time I went
into the kitchen or the bathroom. But in Milan it's easier to
build a skyscraper without a permit than it is to widen a door
or fix a leaky ceiling legally.

I remember the time I went down to City Hall with a
briefcase full of projects and requests and explanations on
legal paper; the idea of enlarging the dormer window even
seemed reasonable to the official who notarized my petitions.
But when I presented my petitions to the idiot down at City
Hall, he acted as if I had proposed moving the Duomo from
the great square to Lambrate. He never said anything really
vulgar to me because I said it all first. So, rather than resort-
ing to the usual person who knows from whom to get what
for a price, I gave up trying to do anything constructive and
continued beaning myself on the rafter between the kitchen
and the bathroom. Given the number of beanings and my
related imprecations, I imagine that by now the petty tyrant

of City Hall must be roasted to a turn down in the last circle
of Hell, if he hasn't been thrown out of there too.

Anyhow, bureaucracy is an evil that infects all cities of
the universe and Milan is, in spite of it, an extraordinary
city, a city that one does not forget, the city that does not
oppress one with the arrogance of its natural beauty or of its
historical monuments, because the most important monument of Milan is the Milanese man, a monument that no one
can destroy.

Margherita too suddenly felt homesick for Milan. "I
would so like to see our old house," she said. "It's been three
years since we visited it."

Then Margherita described the house in Milan to Jo and
gave her a blow-by-blow recapitulation of the appalling
amount of work she had to do to put it in order. Of course
she didn't bother to mention the work I did. "The apartment," she said to Jo, "is three little rooms plus a hall and
facilities. And each room has a bed or a couch to sleep on.
The kitchen has just the right number of things in it. We'll
eat in and we can all sleep there comfortably. A simple
dusting-off and everything will be back to normal in a few
minutes. And then we can go window-shopping and look at
the Christmas decorations, which are something fabulous."

Jo, as a young domestic assistant, particularly feels the
lure of the city. So she answered that it would suit her just
fine if we all went north for a little while.

We found the little house deserted and silent, and since I
had a pretty clear picture of what we were going to find
upstairs, I went ahead of Margherita and Jo. After I un-

locked the door and turned on the light I waited for the scream from Margherita.

It was completely inhuman, her scream. Even if she had found three or four dismembered corpses strewn around she could not have screamed more horrifyingly.

I'm not sure if you can imagine what happens to an apartment in Milan when it's left untouched for three years. If you can bring yourself to think what would happen if a factory smokestack were funneled into three tiny rooms, you wouldn't be far from picturing the sight that tore an inhuman scream from Margherita.

Jo didn't scream because she's a girl with a formidable amount of self-control. Instead she said firmly, "Mrs. Guareschi, that simple little dusting-off that's going to set everything to rights in a few minutes is for you to do. I'd rather walk back to Parma."

"Not necessary," I reassured her. "In order to clean anything in here it would have to be stripped to the bare wood, and the floor would have to be pulled up, new furniture brought in, and all the fixtures changed."

Once Margherita had gotten over the horror of it all, she decided that she wanted to see the rest of the apartment. I handed her one pair of rubber gloves, gave another to Jo, and put the third on myself. I had providently brought them from home. Then I opened the first door.

My little study was buried under a horrendous black, oily pall. Long black spider's-webs dangled lugubriously from the walls and ceiling: they looked like bats.

"My curtains!" Margherita shrieked.

The two black tatters that were hanging at the sides of the glass doors to the balcony were frightening.

Margherita picked her way across the room to the door to my bedroom. She extended her hand toward the doorknob and then pulled it back.

"I'm scared," she said with a shudder.

"Of what?"

"Of finding something awful and vile on top of the bed."

"Like what?"

"Your ghost."

I opened the door and turned on the light. My ghost wasn't stretched out on top of the monstrous black catafalque that had once been my bed. But I swear, even I was afraid of finding it there.

We got out of there as fast as we could. Outside the house, Jo confessed, "You know, for a moment *I* was afraid we were going to find your ghost there, which is nonsense because you were standing right in front of me."

"It's not nonsense at all, Jo," I answered. "Everybody leaves a little portion of his ghost everywhere."

"It's like a Hitchcock story," Jo said shivering.

It was already dark, but we left immediately for the country. Nobody said a word until Piacenza. Then, when we had crossed the Po, Jo broke the silence. "It gives me the chills just to think about it," she said. "Imagine, what if your ghost really had been there!"

"We had a narrow escape!" Margherita said with strong conviction.

...And April Has Thirty-One

☼

I'd slept poorly that night. Sleeping poorly for me means puttering about in pajamas all night long in my study and files, looking over old photographs and heaps of papers that, though they're little more than ten years old, seem at least a century old. Then I take an aspirin with a jigger of cognac because the fresh air has made me sneeze. Then I take a sedative, since my heart has started beating like a machine gun on account of the first pill. Then I need a glass of cold orange juice because the cognac and the first pill have sent my temperature skyrocketing. After a while, because the cold drink has upset my stomach and the sedative has weakened my heartbeat, I make myself some tea and drink a pint of it along with a heart pill. Inevitably, when it's tickled like that, my heart starts to act up again and a hot flash bathes me in sweat. Fortunately it's a fresh, serene night and I can go out on the terrace and smoke my thirty-fifth cigarette of the day. Which brings my stomach back into the game and my old ulcer rears its ugly head again. So I go back inside; now's the time for a Molotov Cocktail (a tremendous spoonful of bicarbonate of soda stuffed down dry and exploded in the stomach by a tall glassful of hot lemonade). I celebrate my liberation and stretch out on the bed.

I search for the most comfortable position. Lying on my left side won't do because of the heart, lying on the right won't do because of the liver, lying face down is impossible because I can't breathe.

My body has three unfortunate dimensions and you might compare it to a polygonal volume with a front, a back, a right side, a left side, a top, and a bottom. That leaves me two possibilities: to curl up with my head lowered and my feet raised, or vice versa.

But I haven't the slightest command of yoga and anyway, could one consider oneself curled up if one were standing on one's feet or on one's head?

I go back to puttering about in my study.

I discover a box full of letters I never opened. I open a few; they're from twenty years ago, all sent on the eve of the historic election of 1948. The first letter describes as "incredible" the following fact: "Just think that in my village the mayor is a man who murdered a poor fellow . . ." Instead I think that I did myself a favor not opening that letter when it arrived. I could never have brought myself to write him the proper reply: "That's nothing, dear friend. What would you say if in twenty years' time a man who murdered masses of people who had fought at his side but didn't agree with him politically was suddenly elected to the Senate?"

In the second envelope I found a 1,000-lira banknote, one of those old ones, big as bed sheets. Some poor soul sent it to me as a contribution to help found my own political party.

Such ingenuousness and trust are touching. I think about framing the banknote and the letter.

The third letter is from a mother who tells me about her son lost in Russia and asks me to keep on with my fight: "Don't get tired of talking about those boys! It may not do any good, but at least it gives us poor mothers the illusion that somebody remembers our dear sons . . . Your pamphlet with the skeleton dressed as a soldier behind the wire fence of a Russian concentration camp made me cry. Yes, I'll vote against them, for his sake . . ."

A pang of grief shakes me when I think about those poor forgotten bones over which grain is now growing. I leave the rest of the old letters unopened and go to look for the little American pills for the liver.

Stuck to the inside of the medicine cabinet doors are some newspaper stories, photographs, and postcards that remind me of my dead companions. And how many there are too! It seems that the inside of all the cabinets' doors are covered with that sort of memorabilia.

In cases like this the proper remedy is the Balanced Cocktail: three little liver pills, one tablespoonful of bicarbonate shot down dry, one tumbler of whisky, one cup of hot tea with lemon, and to top it off, a few cigarettes.

Giving your head a good rubdown with scalding hot water also helps.

The scale is right here in the room with me; I might as well weigh myself. 170 pounds. Too much for my height. It must be on account of that boiled potato I eat every night as a main course after a little cup of rice in broth. I *refuse* to give it up. "You have to live dangerously" was written on the walls of my youth. "Don't stew, BURN!" "*Memento audere semper."* "Never deny your fatherland, conquer it instead." There were so many things written on the walls of my youth. My head is whirling; it doesn't even seem my own any more.

Ful the dog bays, warning me from down there in the courtyard that the sky is growing lighter.

To make a clean round of it, I should now crank up my old Gramophone and put on the turntable my ancient recording of Saint-Saëns' *Danse macabre,* place the needle on the last part, where the music describes the dawn and the skeletons going beddy-bye.

It's too much trouble. I'm going beddy-bye myself without musical accompaniment.

As I said, I'd slept poorly that night. Sleeping poorly for me means being awake all night long and falling into the abyss of exhaustion when the sun is born. And waking up with a start half an hour later, after dreaming that my bicycle has been stolen or I've failed my final exams before graduation. This kind of dream leaves me in such a state of shock and anguish that I'm compelled to jump out of bed and run to check and see if I still have the diploma which says I passed them in July 1928; and there's my bicycle, leaning up against the wall. These stupid dreams recur and have no hidden meanings since my bicycle actually was stolen when I was a boy and since I still cannot persuade myself that I was able to pass those impossible exams, given the colossal ass that I am, and my unsurpassed lack of cleverness.

When I sleep poorly, upon awakening I dawdle for hours in my dressing gown in my own rooms till I finally dress quick as a flash and come downstairs like an unexploded bomb, ready to be set off by the least gust of air.

Around eleven I came down, charged into the kitchen, and glanced around. If I'd seen so much as a picture hanging crooked on the wall or a sloppily folded newspaper there would have been a repetition of what happened to Hiroshima.

Fortunately everything was in place, not a picture tilted, not a newspaper sloppily folded. My mail was neatly stacked in the center of the great oak table, and the floor was clean as a whistle but without a trace of the maddening wax that I inevitably slip on.

Everything in perfect shape: on the mantelpiece, the brass candlesticks were polished and in each stood a fresh white candle, straight as a die. The calendar was turned to the proper date: "Tuesday—30 April."

Margherita and Jo didn't seem to have noticed me. There's nothing that irritates me more, in this situation, than to be told good morning and asked if I want anything.

Ahah. But the mail, the confounded mail might turn the trick. Sometimes a single letter can do it; an insensitive note or a stupid postcard can poison your whole day.

There was a telegram and I opened it first—nothing wrong with it, just the usual desperate plea for an article I hadn't sent off yet.

Then bills to pay, an admonition to send in my tax money immediately, and five letters filled with vicious insults about my latest article.

Everything was normal, in other words; nothing to upset me. It was as if some marvelously intelligent secretary had

gone through the mail to remove anything that might
annoy me.

I didn't see a few magazines that I subscribe to.

"They haven't come," Margherita explained. "There
must be a mail strike. That mail is all yesterday's second
delivery. You didn't come down for supper last night. You
ate upstairs, if you'll remember."

"I know. Everything sat on top of my stomach, as always
happens when I eat alone in a bad humor. What are we
having today?"

Jo showed me the day's menu; everything on it was
exactly what I would have chosen myself.

"Fine!" I exclaimed. "Remember, Jo, if anyone tries to
come over, get rid of them. I don't want to see anybody
today."

"Don't worry," Jo said. "I'll take care of everything."

Just at that moment came a knock at the door and Jo ran
to see who it was. I heard the girl's irritated voice; she
seemed to be arguing with somebody and Margherita sped
off toward the front door. But she didn't get there in time.
Two seconds later my friend Francesco invaded the room.
Francesco was carrying something elegantly wrapped and
his wife had a mountain of carnations clutched to her breast.

"Imagine!" Francesco roared impetuously. "Just imagine
my believing our Giovanni isn't at home! Today of all
days!"

Everybody has his own hail-fellow-well-met, all-invading
friend whom he would gladly kill if he had a chance.
Francesco is that kind of friend. He immediately noticed the
calendar. "What do you mean, the 30th of April! Bring
yourself up to date, man!"

He headed for the calendar but I stopped him with a shout. "I don't need you to turn pages for me! Everybody here has slaved to hide anything that might remind me what day it is and suddenly you have to come charging in and ruin everything. I know perfectly well that it's not April 30th but May 1st and that it's my sixtieth birthday."

"Happy birthday, Giovanni," and the imbecile began to sing.

"Drop dead," I cut in. "You and your wife and your sixty carnations and your French bubbly can all go to hell in a wheelbarrow."

They both left, shocked and offended (taking their champagne and flowers with them), and I realized that I would never see them again, thank God.

Margherita and Jo looked at me worriedly. But the bomb had already exploded and I found my blood pressure was back to normal.

"Everything's all right," I said happily. "It's still April 30th."

And so we gaily celebrated the 30th of April.

Thirty days has September, June, and November; all the rest have thirty-one, including April when necessary.

My Date with Gramigna

✻

Every year on Christmas Eve I have a date with Gramigna. The last of his kind, Gramigna is a tiny boy with a rascal's face and a smock that's grown too tight and too short for him. His book bag hangs around his neck the way students carried them in days gone by; in the pocket of his smock there is a slingshot—a forked elmwood stick, the elastics made out of slices of inner tube and leading to a leather square that holds the stones—the tongue from one of his father's old boots.

Gramigna is an old-fashioned schoolboy but a little spoiled by modernity since he wears low oxfords instead of the cleated cavalry boots worn in my day—perfect, in the wintertime, for sliding across the ice in ditches alongside the rocky roads leading to school. Boots made of cowhide, sturdy stuff, not calfskin or shammy (what a disillusionment when I found out that it's properly spelled *chamois!*).

Ah, those were the days.

So every year I have a date with Gramigna on Christmas Eve, and it's very comforting.

It's true that I'm old, but I'm not a crybaby or one of those men who breaks down and sobs when he returns to a favorite childhood haunt and finds something destroyed or changed. But I will confess that the first time I returned to Parma I went by train, because I had lost the war and as a consequence they had taken away my first car bought on installments. I was appalled to find, in the great square across from the railroad station, not the colossal monument to Verdi but horrendous apartment houses. I was appalled because, while I knew I had lost the war, I didn't realize Giuseppe Verdi had also lost it. I simply couldn't understand why the monument to Verdi, damaged by the American bombers, hadn't been repaired and was replaced instead with these dreadful buildings.

Then I quickly mastered the principles of democratic logic which I wouldn't have known otherwise, having grown up under a dictatorship. Therefore I wasn't shocked any more when I saw place after place in Parma where the "liberator's pickax" (as opposed to the "purifier's pickax" of dictatorship) had torn down something dear to me. Naturally I felt it. But, I repeat, I'm not an old crybaby and I maintain that a man's life loses nothing even if a cataclysm completely changes the face of the places where he spent his childhood. In fact it's ultimately useful because when in old age you see the supposedly delightful haunts of your youth, it becomes immediately apparent how really shabby and miserable they were and how much less fascinating than the image kept in the pigeon-holes of your memory. A boy's eyes see quite differently than the tired, disenchanted eyes of an old man.

Let me give you an example.

A twenty-five-year-old boy goes off to war. He's been married for a year and already has a darling baby boy two years old, from which fact you may determine for yourselves the passionate nature of his love for his wife.

He leaves and the young, beautiful wife accompanies him to the train, where she says to him, "I'll wait for you!" They send this boy to Africa where he's captured by the enemy. After the war ends, he manages to get wind of a fabulous business deal. He writes to his wife: "I've been given the opportunity to make a secure future for us and the baby and I want to take advantage of it." She writes back: "Stay there. I'll wait for you."

So he stays, and twenty-five years after his departure he comes home, loaded with money. He finds the new house and presses the doorbell, his heart close to bursting. A few moments later, he finds himself in front of a mature lady with gray hair and bony, nervous hands full of thick veins.

"You didn't wait for me!" he says to her, deeply disappointed. Then a hulking brute of a young man with a beard comes in, light years different from the beautiful tot left behind twenty-five years before. The child himself hadn't expected to change so much.

I don't know what this little story means because I don't understand anything about psychology and philosophy. All I know is that now, when I go home to my city, I feel like somebody who's been asleep for thirty years and wakes up to find himself in a completely unrecognizable world. In fact, I can walk for hours through streets I've never seen, looking in vain for one wall I recognize. But this isn't what disturbs me. I wouldn't care about physical change if I could see faces from days gone by. There's no point in making polemics about their destroying old, beautiful palaces to build in their places vile reinforced concrete monstrosities.

It would be more useful, if it could be done, to make polemics against whoever it is that destroys young men and women bursting with beauty and health and replaces them with wrinkled, bald, toothless, rheumy old people.

It's a far better idea to walk along the modern city streets looking at the young people today than to hunt around for ghosts in streets that haven't yet been contaminated. Ghosts. What's the most depressing and sad spectacle that greets my eyes when I return to my city? The sight of the Duomo, the Baptistry, the Pilotta, the university, the Steccata church, the Regio Theatre, and so forth. What are those strange ghosts doing in the middle of the city of great department stores, supermarkets, in the modern city in which the perfume of the sweet violets of Parma has been replaced by the exhaust from 300,000 automobiles?

They ought to take them apart piece by piece and reconstruct them in a special precinct on the outskirts of town. You can say all you want about artistic heritage, historical witness, tourist attractions—but first tell me what it is the tourist looks for the moment he drives into town.

He looks for a place to park his car. Let's give it to him, then. And let us also give him, neatly gathered together, the principal monuments and the possibility of visiting them in a few short minutes.

Every year on Christmas Eve I go to meet Gramigna. And he is always punctual, always the same, standing straight on the granite pedestal beneath which his old teacher rests—my mother.

Gramigna is the last of his kind and the sculptor has gone so far as to say so on the pedestal.

Gramigna is there waiting for me. His book bag hangs around his neck, and the bag's strap falls freely away from his body; and between the strap and his smock there's a small space where I always find a little bouquet of flowers.

Gramigna is on time and my being able to find him ever unchanged consoles me for the changes I have noticed driving through the city on my way to the Marore Cemetery. But how long will it last? The city is expanding and day by day it creeps closer to the tiny section that is trying hard not to become a suburb of the city. The dead people are marking time though.

Anyhow, the dead are community property, and you don't argue with the community. I wouldn't be a bit surprised one day to find in Gramigna's place the pump of a gas station, much more useful and profitable than a grave. There are no surprises left in a city that doesn't think twice before destroying a monument to Verdi to make space for a condominium apartment house.

The fate of the first of his kind, Verdi, and the last of his kind, Gramigna, is melancholy but logical. And it follows the strictest process of social leveling.

The last time I went to the appointment Gramigna's head and shoulders were sprinkled with white. The wind had brought swarms of snow moths from far away and it was hard to strike a match.

"What's happened to you, boy?" the old teacher asked me. "Are those white hairs I see?"

"No," I said. "It's just snow."

"Well then, put your beret back on or you'll catch a cold."

"Any news?" the teacher's husband asked.

I knew how to please him so I told him that they'd put a

100,000-lira note into circulation with Manzoni's picture on it. He was very happy about this and began to recite: "Farewell, you mountains, water's source . . ."

"Don't make him waste time!" the old teacher chastized her husband. "He should go home right away; it'll be dark soon." You don't argue with an old teacher so I left.

"Merry Christmas and Happy 1968, Gramigna," I whispered, walking around the big block of granite. "Tell me, who is it that always puts a bouquet in the strap of your book bag?"

"I do!" Gramigna growled.

Part Two

Stories About Jo

How It All Began

✳

One fine Wednesday is when it all began. The establishment (if you could call a complex of barracks sunk into an old abandoned cave an "establishment") was several kilometers from the nearest populated area, but it was easy to get to because, as had been explained to us, all you had to do was follow the odor.

In fact, once we had left the highway and were on our way down the first dirt road to the left, an acrid odor hit our noses. "It's not an odor," Margherita amended. "It's a *stench*. 'Odor' is too literary and doesn't convey the true effect. It's like the difference between 'distasteful' and 'disgusting.' "

The effect of the odor, which was in fact a stench of the most disgusting kind, as we slowly but surely crept toward its source, was that it increased in intensity inch by inch until even the car motor started to gag.

Anyhow, the establishment was a cluster of corrugated tin barracks aligned along the four sides of a huge workyard. From a smokestack gushed a dense yellow smoke with red trimmings. A heavy smoke that surged up to an impossibly low altitude, spread out, and settled down to form a lid over that infernal caldron. The gatekeeper, sensitive to bribes, answered our questions. The person we were interested in was a worker at this stink factory. It was around twelve noon. In a few minutes she would be coming out and he promised to point her out to us.

In the vast workyard there were moving shapes that, in their general outlines, recalled the human form. These were buzzing around large trucks and were loading, in a cloud of poisonous powder, sacks of the finished product, or unloading in a cloud of flies, bones, hooves, and other bovine and equine relics. Others were pushing around carts of one or the other mess.

"Look there, it's her!" the gatekeeper exclaimed after a while, opening the gatehouse door and pointing to one of the cart pushers.

"Which one, Giovanni?" Margherita asked me under her breath. "The one in front or the one behind?"

"The one behind," I answered. "The one in front is the wheelbarrow."

"Jo," the gatekeeper yelled from his window, "there're two people here looking for you."

"Okay!" it yelled back. The person answering to the name Jo didn't stop but made a nodding gesture, which proved my observation that the human being was the shape behind.

At that moment the siren began to shriek and instantly the person named Jo abandoned the wheelbarrow in the middle of the workyard and headed for the gatehouse.

"It certainly has quick reflexes," Margherita said. "It didn't lose a tenth of a second. It must be extremely efficient. That's why I'm guessing it's a 'she,' because there's no other way of knowing."

I couldn't disagree with her, because there was simply no objective basis on which to make an evaluation. The person was wearing overalls, a handkerchief around its neck, a second handkerchief knotted under its chin to cover its hair, a third handkerchief knotted behind its head to cover its face from its chin to its eyes. A bicyclist's beret, the beak turned around backwards, covered its forehead. Its eyes were covered by welder's goggles. Heavy gloves covered its hands and tall rubber boots its feet. I am, however, going to go along with Margherita's guess (and my own hindsight) and refer to this person as "she."

"Are you the people who want to talk to me?" she asked after she joined us.

"If your name is Miss Gioconda Cicon, yes," Margherita answered.

"It is, if you don't mind," she answered. "If you, instead of getting kicks riding around in a car, had to work up to your nose in this dust and this smell, you wouldn't be so concerned about elegance."

She had taken off her goggles and a few of the handkerchiefs and now we were certain that she was a woman.

"Now then, we," Margherita began, "are in need of a person—"

"If you're looking for a servant, you can get lost," Jo interrupted her. "I'm not going to be a chambermaid, not for a million lire a month. I have my professional pride and my independence and my own personality!"

I took command of the operation. "You've misunderstood us. We're not looking for a servant. We're looking for a person who is young, intelligent, polite, different, a person like you, in other words, to give some tone to our house, which is rather depressing and poorly arranged, and (no offense to my wife) badly organized and managed. Something more than an assistant, I think; in fact, an 'animator' if the term doesn't put you off."

It didn't put her off at all. " 'Animator'? In what sense?" she said coolly.

"Look," I explained, "in the animated drawing industry, the animator is the man who gives life to the figures with a series of designs which describe every fraction of a movement that the figures must accomplish. In the, let us say, worldly realm, the animator is the person who, with her spirit, her communicative cordiality, her discoveries, gives life and liveliness to the dancing soirees and the musical comedies; who succeeds, in other words, in linking with invisible wires—"

"Franco Zeffirelli is the name," Jo cut in.

"Exactly!" I exclaimed. "We're going out of our minds looking for a female Zeffirelli to choreograph all the dissonances in our house and make life more bearable for us."

"On this basis, we can continue to discuss the idea," said Jo. "One thing before we start discussing details: if the house isn't in the city, no deal."

"It's in the country, but you will have at your disposal a small, charming Spider," I answered.

"Okay, since I've got a driver's license. Number Two: private bedroom with bath."

"All our bedrooms have their own bath."

"Three: personal TV with both channels. I have my own personality, my own interior world, my own inclinations and

I don't want to suppress them by watching, for example, News Roundup on Channel Two when there's a Rita Pavone special on One, or vice versa. Four: personal transistor radio."

"It's fine with us."

"Do you have children?"

"Two. The boy is twenty-four years old, already gone from home, and married."

"That's good. That way I don't run the risk of marrying him myself. Anyhow I don't want any grandchildren underfoot."

"There aren't any grandchildren yet."

"Okay, but give me ample notice. What about the girl?"

"She's eighteen."

"A debutante?"

"No, she made her debut last month. Her birthday is in November."

"Your wife, is she understanding or authoritarian?"

"We've only been married twenty-five years and I don't yet know."

She laughed and asked us to follow her into the administrative offices. When we got her home, finally, she thought the house was passable and her personal room acceptable. The TV and transistor radio pleased her very much. At lunch we invited her to eat with us in the breakfast room. She said she wasn't prepared to give up her personal freedom and insisted on eating in the kitchen. She thought Margherita was an execrable cook and took over the kitchen herself. At night, after she finished her work she went to hide in her room. But around 8:30, when Margherita, Passionaria, and I took up position in front of the TV, the Animator reappeared.

"Isn't your TV working?" I asked.

"Yes, it works," she said drily. "However, if you don't mind, I'd rather not be treated like a leper. I shall watch TV with you. Besides, I like dialogue."

Thus the Animator began following the happenings on TV along with our family and still does. I have to say this to prevent some crackpot out there, following these little TV chronicles, from accusing us of being antisocial egoists who deny their dependents the most important rights.

"Tonight Marchesi's on," the Animator announced. "I'll watch the Carousel and then I'm going to bed. It's a real drag."

"I disagree," I objected. "That show is a smiling pause in the week's moroseness."

"More than a pause, it's a menopause," Margherita put in. "Given the age of the principal performers. And then Marchesi has become a bit rarefied, too literary, too intellectual. For example, will somebody please tell me the meaning of that poem we had last time: 'How charming/ The poster/ On the altar:/ "We pray you/ Will pray here." ' "

I answered that it was a delicate question. "Marchesi is an unsuppressible punster. 'To Be Good or Prosper: the Village's Question'—apart from everything else, it has the grace and freshness of our local athletic club. It reminds me of Ernesto—he was a veritable cannon of puns. One day Ernesto, who was a bank clerk, had to go on an errand to the Bologna mint and I asked him a pick up for me a thousand freshly minted 10-lira notes for a practical joke I wanted to play. As soon as he got there, he turned in all the used and crumbly notes—including the 10,000-lira note I gave him—and sat down to wait for them to issue him new notes. Just then a flash fire broke out and they all evacuated the building, which was severely burned. So when Ernesto came home with no money, all he did was laugh and say, Gone with the Mint, Gone with the Mint."

"I don't understand," Margherita said nastily.

"You don't understand the joke, *Gone with the Wind* becomes Gone with the Mint?"

"What's this Ernesto doing now?"

"Now he tells stories on TV," Passionaria cut in. "Here's one. There's an animal in Tibet called a nam, similar to the gnu. A Buddhist priest was lost in the hills one day and it began to snow. As the nam was fond of the priest, it went off into the hills to search for him. A day later the nam returned, the poor priest clinging to its back. Naturally the nam would be rewarded for this, since the Tibetan villagers loved their priest as much as did the nam. So they decided to give the nam the food it loved most dearly and cover it with laurels and make a statue to honor it. The food it loved most dearly was hearts of gnu. On the appointed festival day the statue of the nam was unveiled, the nam itself was covered with laurel leaves, and finally the gnu heart was brought out. Unfortunately overnight some maggots had gotten into it and made holes throughout. But the nam was simply satisfied to have his favorite dish and ate it anyway. Ernesto ends the tale with its title: The Commended Nam Ate a Mealy Heart."

Margherita sat in stunned silence for a moment and then said, "Let us hope this Ernesto never shows his face at our door."

Thoughts of an Unwed Mother

☼

Jo, by now established as our TV navigator, approached us one evening with measured steps.

"I hear via the grapevine," she said to Margherita, "that your son's going to have a baby."

"That's odd," Margherita said with unforgivable frivolity, "what I heard was that his wife was going to have it."

"This is no time for sparkling wit, Mrs. Guareschi," the girl answered. "It was made perfectly clear to you: no children underfoot, at least not *my* feet."

"Now Jo, we haven't broken our agreement. It's not our fault that our son doesn't stick to it, since he doesn't live under our roof."

"That's irrelevant," the girl answered. "I know the geriatric mentality through and through. The minute a grandchild comes into the picture, they turn into cretins. Therefore let's get one thing clear: enter grandchild, exit Jo."

"Okay," I said. "That's simple enough. Whenever our son or daughter-in-law comes to show us the baby, we'll look at him in the courtyard."

"What if it's raining?" said Margherita worriedly.

"This is a matter of principle," I explained to her. "And you don't want to complicate matters of principle with atmospheric conditions."

"True," Margherita said. "But it's immoral to leave a poor baby exposed to the elements. I thought the proletariat was more generous."

"The proletariat," Jo snapped, "is more generous than the bourgeoisie. If it rains, he can come in."

This was a foot in the door as far as we were concerned and it was relatively easy to extract further concessions from her as far as hail, snow, and wind storms went.

"However," Jo said severely, "the child stays only as long as absolutely necessary."

Don't be shocked at Jo's tone of ultimatum; just remember that, today being what it is and things being the way they are, it's a simple thing to get a grandchild and an impossible one to find a domestic.

Margherita wouldn't let well enough alone. "Jo, what can you possibly have against a child that isn't even born yet?"

"Mrs. Guareschi," the girl answered, "if I brought my baby girl here to fill your house with screaming, wet diapers, and chaos, would you like it?"

"No."

"All right, if you wouldn't like my daughter around, then I won't like your grandchild. Or is it that according to you your grandchild should have something better than my daughter? Are we going to have yet another appalling example of class privilege? As far as that goes, I know one thing: when I brought my baby to be baptized, she was dressed better than a millionaire's daughter. And I'll tell you that when it's time for her to make her first communion she'll have a fantastic dress. I want my daughter to enjoy all the most beautiful and satisfying things in the world. Even if I have to spend 200,000 lire for the dress."

"You won't do it," I said.

"I will too! I've already started to save the money and I'll have plenty of time to collect the whole amount."

"No, Jo," I tried to explain softly. "You won't have time. Not because of the money but because it won't be allowed any more. In lots of big cities, and the trend is making inroads into the smaller cities too, the idea of the equality of all men before God is becoming very popular. Hence we already have only one-class baptisms, weddings, and funerals. In Turin, for example, they're talking about making a rule that all kids have to take first communion dressed in the same kind of clothes. 'It would be more in keeping,' say the Authorities, 'with the religious and other-worldly significance of the sacrament.' Which means it's a sure thing that in a few years there will be regulation dress for first communion, no modifications or improvements allowed. Of course I'm sure there will be one such outfit for boys and one for girls, unless they design a kind of 'eucharistic overalls' that would serve as well for both sexes. This way, you see, your daughter will be able to have a dress as fine as a millionaire's, without your spending all that money."

Jo shook her head. "Nonsense. My daughter will have the prettiest dress of all and I'll have her picture taken in it big enough to frame. My girl will have a 200,000-lira dress. It's my money, which I earn with my own hands and save by giving up things for myself. And it's my right to spend it any way I choose."

"Nobody's stopping you. But it might be better spent, for example, if you bought a nice bed for your house . . ."

"Sure! And what about my little girl, on the day of her first communion do I send her around with the bed wrapped around her? Don't you understand, your first communion dress is the first of the three greatest satisfactions a woman can have? After that comes the wedding dress, and finally comes the baptismal robes for the baby. Nobody's going to stop me from fulfilling my role as a mother!"

"Jo, if they make a certain dress regulation for all first communions, your child won't be able to go inside the church with a different dress on. It would be like a soldier wearing a uniform that didn't match his comrades'."

"This is another instance of tyrannizing the working class!" Jo shouted. "A rich child can turn her nose up at a first communion dress because she has millions of other satisfactions to look forward to. But a poor girl, the child of a humble servant like me, why shouldn't she be able to experience the few satisfactions alloted to her miserable station in life? Why should Jo Cicon, humble servant, allow her daughter to miss a fantastic day she'll remember all her life?"

"Jo, the bishop will say, 'Before the altar all children are created equal.' "

"Admirable reasoning! Before the altar everybody's the same, but old Tizio's daughter has a shiny Alfa Romeo double-parked outside the church, while my daughter only has her run-down everyday shoes. It's fine, my daughter and old Tizio's wearing the same dress at their first communion; of course every other day of the year Tizio's daughter runs around in Dior gowns and mink stoles while my daughter wears worker's overalls or a coat with a catskin collar." Jo's anger was very convincing. "How about you, Mrs. Guareschi?" she shouted. "Do you remember your first communion dress?"

"Certainly," Margherita answered. "It was simply marvelous even if the shoes did kill my feet."

"You see, even your wife agrees with me," she turned back to me.

"I agree with you too," I said, "but I can't do anything about it because I'm not a bishop, much less a cardinal."

"Well, can't you write about it in your column?"

"It wouldn't do any good. The only thing that would is TV."

Jo started laughing. "You're talking about lessons in how frozen fish tastes better than fresh and how we're always moving from Good to Better. As usual, it would be an advertising campaign aimed at defrauding the poor, and instead of spending 200,000 lire I'd wind up spending 230,000 lire."

"What for?"

"Thirty thousand for the regulation first communion uniform, and 200,000 for a fantastic dress to put on right after the ceremony. So you see it's always me that winds up paying, because you know for sure none of those rich people are going to bother buying anything but the 30,000-lira uniform."

"Jo—" I started.

"No!" Margherita howled. "If you give her a raise every week it will wind up with us working for her."

Jo looked at us with pity. "A woman who puts dishes in

the washing machine and a man who prefers Bellini to the Beatles. Don't worry, I'd never hire you."

Then her tone changed and her eyes got all dreamy and she whispered, "Two blond angels . . . two children dressed like angels holding up the lace trains of their white gowns . . . Nobody's ever done it before in my town. It'll cost as much as 270,000. But I'll make it."

Why She Chose
the Name "Vera Dry"

✵

Now what would this 'consumer culture' be?" Jo treacherously asked me one afternoon.

Unthinkingly, I took the bait. "This new life system of the Society of Prosperity, meaning us," I answered. "Before, people wanted to work more to earn more to be able to save more. Now, people want to work less to earn more to be able to spend more."

"Sounds perfectly reasonable to me," Jo said, and we were off to the races.

"Yes, but only as long as being able to spend more doesn't turn into a kind of slavery."

"Which means what?"

"It means that if I don't feel like going on a weekend or buying a new car every two or three years or going to those hateful little 'get-togethers' of my next-door neighbors, I don't have to."

"So who's forcing you?"

"Nobody, yet. But when prosperity brings us up to the level of the United States, a person won't be able to refuse without being judged, as happens in the United States today, a pauper or a misanthrope."

Jo shook her head. "Nonsense. Each country has its own personality. It will never happen here."

"The only people who will be saved are those who are old enough to have a well-defined personality. But what about the kids growing up in this atmosphere? Jo, don't you already see so many young people wandering around sad and lost in a world they can't love because it's been reduced to matter and emptied of any spirituality or myths and hence lacks hope? Think of how many young people have to live in groups because they're so afraid that, if they're left alone, all they'll see is the great vacuum."

Jo stared at me in shock. "Of course when you're alone you have only the great vacuum to look at! You tell me, then: when you're alone, what's there to do?"

"Think."

"Some fun!" the girl laughed.

"Don't you like movies?"

"Sure, but that's entirely different. At the movies I follow a story with situations, characters, places, etc. etc."

"Every human being," I said softly, "has within himself enough of that sort of material to churn out thousands of films much more interesting than the ones shown in the theater, because the protagonist is always you."

The girl looked at me with sincere pity. "I see. The usual waking dreams."

"Not at all. What I'm talking about is constructing organic stories, with a solid foundation in reality. Each human being has within himself tendencies and aspirations, convictions, desires, hopes, feelings, resentments, ambitions, experiences—every ingredient necessary to construct a story to tell to yourself. Naturally you write your own dialogue with other people line by line, and each situation is logically set up and resolved. When you start a production like this inside your own head, you'll find it's a pleasure to have some time to yourself."

"It's wasted time and brainwork," Jo decided.

"Maybe, for somebody with sawdust for brains. But for somebody with an ordinary mind who knows himself, he would never go beyond what is strictly possible for himself. That way your 'fantasies' can also have some practical application. Inside the mind of any normal being, there's already a series of films in operation, which you could call This Is the Life I'd Like to Live. Films that are run through, projected, and modified continually following the large or small happenings in which the subject finds himself involved. But the general theme remains the same. Remember that these fantasy films always have two spectators: you and your subconscious mind. And the subconscious never forgets that film, so that when it becomes aware that in real life you have the possibility of coming closer to the path you're following in your private film, your subconscious will push you in the direction of those little turns and detours that will help you to get on the path."

Jo thought the idea over calmly. "I think I'll try it out," she said, disappearing into her room.

For two days Jo was quiet as a mouse, but it was obvious that she was very perplexed. The third day she let the cat out of the bag to Margherita.

"Mrs. Guareschi," she said, "would it be true-to-life if I

were to spend a holiday at Tabiano and run into some fellow
from Rome who'd come to clear up his lung congestion?"

"Certainly," Margherita answered. "With national health
insurance, half of Italy goes to Tabiano and Salsomaggiore
for a breath of fresh air."

"He didn't come on his health insurance," the girl explained. "He's a very famous movie director."

Margherita burst out laughing. "I could have sworn it! Is
there a girl in the world that doesn't daydream about finding
a director who'll tell her, 'I'm going to make you the biggest
movie star in film history'?"

"That's not it at all!" the girl protested. "I'm staying
right within the bounds of possibility. He's about to make a
brilliant art film—the story of a miserable servant girl who
inherits two billion dollars, becomes very famous, and
amuses herself by mistreating people who give themselves
airs. Don't you think it's highly possible that a director
would choose a servant girl to play the role of the servant
girl?"

"It would be more true-to-life if the director cast a
servant girl in the role of a duchess," Margherita observed.
"Have you signed the contract yet?"

"No, before I throw myself into the world of the cinema I
want to give it some serious thought."

From then on, Jo was hooked by the game. She took
advantage of every free moment to scamper off to her room
so that she could mentally work on her story. One day she
confronted me. "I'm undecided about my stage name," she
said. "Which do you prefer: Rosa Colt or Vera Dry?"

"Rosa Colt is too cowboy," Margherita commented.
"Vera Dry sounds more like a vermouth than an actress."

I said that I liked it best for that reason, because it conveyed the impression of a sophisticated artist.

A few days of intense mental labor for Jo went by. Now she was so deep in thought that she spoke only in monosyllables. Finally she confessed to Margherita. "Vera Dry is finished," she said dramatically. "I thought he was a marvelous man, and it turns out he's nothing but a dirty rat."

Margherita shook her head. "I knew it was going to end like this. The usual naïve starlet deceived by the usual handsome cad. It happens every day in the movie world."

"You've got it all wrong," the girl said. "This is a different situation entirely. I've made six films and I'm a world-famous star now. I've earned my Ferrari, my Rolls-Royce, my Mediterranean villa, to say nothing of the jewels. Then, like an idiot, I fell in love with him and he betrayed me for some two-bit starlet. I threw him out like a dog."

"And now, of course, you're going on to work with another director."

"No, I've had enough of the movies. It's a filthy world and it's not for me. Now I'm living in Paris where I've opened a fantastic dress shop. I had the good luck of discovering a cute trick named Godfrey who's an absolute bang-up dress designer and business is in full swing. To tell you the truth, Godfrey and I are getting quite chummy, so don't be shocked if we get married."

"Now watch your step, Jo," Margherita said seriously. "This Godfrey character doesn't sound very solid."

As usual Margherita was right and, after two days of gloomy silence, Jo confided her sad story: Godfrey turned the tables on her and eloped with the tritest imaginable Swedish model, just as Jo was about to open her fall collection. In fact, he made off with the entire collection, and of course Jo was ruined.

"What did you do then?" Margherita asked.

"I had to sell everything to pay off my debts," Jo explained. "It was as if I'd gone mad. I wandered around Paris all night long, stopping to look down into the black waters of the Seine. Last night I was leaning against the parapet of one of those bridges, and *she* passed by, that Swedish hussy. She saw me, of course, so she stopped to say, 'You can't throw yourself off, Madame. You're not allowed to unload garbage into the Seine.' Any rationality I might have had, left me then. I picked her up by the heels and dropped her over the parapet. 'Oh yes you can,' I said as she disappeared under water."

"Jo," I put in, "it's not a bad story. But just for the sake of telling a good story, you don't bump people off. Not even a Swedish model. Now what are you going to do?"

"Nobody saw me," Jo answered. "I'll live in the shadows. I'll end up as a waitress in a bistro or I'll enlist in the Foreign Legion."

"Jo," Margherita said, "wouldn't it be easier for you to come back here? There'll always be a place for you."

The girl thought it over. "I think I will. But imagine what a humiliation it is, after being queen of the film and fashion worlds, to be reduced to a servant again! There's nothing left of my glorious past."

"There's something left," I said. "Instead of calling you Jo, we'll call you Vera Dry."

"You should be ashamed to open your mouth!" she howled. "It's all your fault. If you hadn't started me in on this thinking business, today I wouldn't have the bitterness of terrible disappointments and the remorse for having killed a woman."

"Killed, my eye!" Margherita said. "All those Swedish girls are athletic and swim like fish—the worst that one got out of it was a sore throat!"

Jo went to bed very relieved.

Misadventures in Miniskirt

For at least a month Jo had been fretting, making mysterious phone calls and lightning trips to the city. Finally one day I said to Margherita: "Have you got an idea about what that girl's up to?"

"No, and I'm not interested to know either. It's a question of her privacy. Everybody's entitled to his own private life."

"That's fine, Margherita, if they use their own car and not my Spider which is a part of *my* private life."

"That Spider is a child's toy, not for serious people," Margherita retorted.

I dropped the subject. I couldn't explain to Margherita that the Spider is the only automobile that merits the name. The true automobile should be bodyless, consisting simply of the chassis, the gear box, and the steering wheel. The interiors of today are a ludicrous compromise between the locomotive and the landau. The automobile was born as a semi-mobile vehicle furnished with a canvas cover for use in emergencies, like an umbrella. The true motorist gets into a car in the same spirit that a rider mounts a horse. The automobile was born in France in 1770 and was topless. The idea of the cabin was invented for the comfort of traveling salesmen who tour around with their competitors hard at their heels—naturally an American idea, spawned by the country which builds the most vulgar, monstrous cars in the world. It amuses me very much when I see the famous old "dream cars" of America, which only the gypsies use here. The difference between people who ride in open cars and those who ride in closed cabins is like the difference between people who eat veal florentine and creatures who enjoy Spam.

What I'm saying is bound to horrify all those who think of the automobile as a bit of home on wheels and like to furnish the interior with Persian blinds, curtains, carpets, radios, TVs, record players, air conditioning, miniature bars, refrigerators, and other such commodities; but, I repeat, the genuine automobile died with the last Torpedo.

Anyhow, to get back to the story. Jo had been busy as a squirrel for about a month and finally I found out why.

"Hey," she said to me, "do you remember when I left my home town like a streak, with a straw suitcase held together with chicken wire and a dress that looked like it had been cut with a pair of garden shears?"

I answered that I remembered it in vivid detail and she whispered: "Wait a second." She disappeared and after a while came back dressed in something that made my eyes pop open. "See?" she exclaimed. "Sunday is the village festival and I'm making my comeback at the wheel of your Spider. I'll park the car in the square in front of the café, get out, sit at a little table, light up a Gauloise, order a whisky, pay with a 1,000-lira bill and leave the rest as tip, throw away the cigarette half-smoked, get back in the Spider, and make my getaway à la James Bond. Can you imagine what they'll say?"

"They'll say you left your skirt at home," Margherita answered.

The truth was, Jo's dress, in spite of being very very Op, had a certain lack: all that was left of her miniskirt was the mini.

"Then at night," the girl went on, "I'll go to the dance in my gold-lamé Goldfinger outfit, complete with rhinestone spangles, and an operatic wig big and red as Rome burning under Nero. I'll give them all apoplexy! What do you say to that?"

"I think you've omitted one important detail," I said. "If I remember correctly your house has a balcony overlooking the street?"

"Sure, but what's that got to do with it?"

"After the dance is over, before you go to bed, you ought to appear in a negligée festooned with mirrors and bicycle reflectors—"

"—not to mention a necklace of Christmas lights strung together," Margherita added. "You can rig up the battery in your brassière."

"But what has your poor village done to you?" I asked.

"Nothing to me, I don't know any of them. I'm doing it for my mother's sake. If you only knew how they made her suffer with their malice when I had my accident in the Fiat."

"You had a car accident?" Margherita asked, astounded.

"The business of my daughter all started in the Fiat of that vile wretch," Jo explained. "But Sunday I'll get even for my mother's sake and give her the greatest satisfaction of her life!"

Margherita is very sentimental and got all teary. "What a noble and generous soul!" she exclaimed. "To comfort her mother she's given up nearly all of her skirt and she wouldn't think twice before giving up the rest of the dress and appearing in the village topless."

"Mrs. Guareschi," the girl exclaimed, "we only have one mother!"

Jo left Sunday morning in my Spider dressed in her phenomenal black-and-white Op outfit.

At lunch, naturally, we talked about Jo.

"If you want my opinion," Margherita said, "they'll withstand the shock of the miniskirt, but, even though they're hearty countryfolk, I imagine there will be some that won't be able to take the gold-lamé Goldfinger outfit."

At that moment the breakfast-room door flew open, and there stood Jo. We looked at her astonished, and even Margherita, on whom it is very difficult to make an impression, let her eyes pop wide open.

From the waist up Jo was still Op, but from the waist down she looked more like Mao's China since she was wearing a pair of blue denim trousers, worn thin, bleached, and ragged at the edges. They were the same pants she had worn when she worked in the glue factory, where Margherita and I had seen her for the first time.

"Jo! What's happened to you?" Margherita said, leaping up.

Jo spread her arms wide. "Even if a girl is wounded to the very depths of her soul, does that give her the right to hit her own mother?"

Turning our thoughts to Jo's mother and to her arms,

which looked more like tree trunks, we answered no. The girl went on to tell us of her tragic misadventure.

"It all started with the heat, which spoiled my make-up," she explained, "so rather than going over to the square first thing, I thought the best idea would be to go home and freshen up a bit. When she laid eyes on me, my mother turned into a raging tiger. Even the baby looked at me as if I were some kind of Martian. I brought her a plastic Pluto the Dog, which terrified her, and she wouldn't even look at the Gemini 9 tricycle I brought her. She started shrieking like a maniac and almost had convulsions. I had to bring the toys back with me."

"What about the television set?"

"I brought it back too. My mother said the baby has all the time she needs to become depraved. 'If you unload that monstrosity, I'll smash it to bits!' is what she screamed at me."

"I get the picture," Margherita said. "All except for the pants."

"You'd understand if you had seen the stick she was waving around. She forced me to put them on. She said rather than having me run around looking like a street-walker, she would kill me."

"I figured that much," Margherita said, "but once you were out of her sight, why didn't you take them off?"

"How?" Jo wailed in desperation. "Can't you see she's tied them on me with steel wire?"

Jo's mother had done an excellent job because she hadn't stopped at wrapping the wire around her daughter's waist but had gone on to manufacture an armature of it encircling the girl's legs. To free Jo I had to run to the garage and arm myself with shears, pliers, and wire-cutters. Even so, it was hard work.

Jo was very sad. "I sacrificed myself to avenge her and look how she rewarded me. She treated me like a lunatic. And she didn't stop at me, either. She said that if you and your wife had lent me your car to send me around looking like this, then you must be the two most immoral people in Italy!"

"But what did I do?" Margherita protested. "Why didn't you tell her that I don't run this household, he does, and I don't count at all?"

"Because it's not true," Jo answered. "Now what am I going to do with that TV?"

"Turn it in for a nice animal," I advised her. "Your mother would like a calf to raise. A milk cow is more profitable, amusing, and instructive than a TV set."

The Mysteries
of Bureaucracy

Jo, who was leafing through my newspapers, burst out laughing. "Hey!" she said, "listen to what just happened in Colorno. A 65-year-old lady went to Dr. So-and-So to get a few prescriptions. She handed him her National Health Insurance booklet and he answered, 'Nothing doing. I just received a notice from the NHI board saying you died on November 25th of last year. You can't use that booklet any more.' So the poor lady goes running over to the local NHI office and tries to explain she didn't die November 25th last, given the fact that she's still alive. 'Certainly,' says the clerk, 'there's clearly an error. It's Dr. So-and-So who died November 25th last.' 'But I spoke to him face-to-face not half an hour ago!' 'I'm sorry,' the clerk said, 'but we get so much official correspondence here.' Isn't that a nice story?"

"It's so old," Margherita answered. "When I was a girl, they told it differently. The director of a hospital goes to visit the ward containing some bricklayers who were recovering from the collapse of the building they were working on. The director is accompanied by the doctor and nurse on duty. Passing in front of the beds, the doctor explains: 'This

one died at 2:15, this one died at 3:11, this one died at
4:30—' 'But I'm still alive!' the 4:30 fellow says. 'Shut up!'
says the nurse. 'You think you know more than the
doctor?' "

Jo shook her head. "Of course. Old jokes that journalists
drag out when they can't think of anything else to fill the
papers with. It's not a very hard job, being a reporter—you
don't even have to work to think up your stories. All you
need is a decent memory. And the people eat it up."

"Jo," I protested, "they may seem like old jokes, but
they're not. Don't you remember hearing about the poor
woman in Avenza who had her pension cut off because she
was supposed to have been dead for a month? And those
girls some clerk erroneously classified 'Male' who wound up
being drafted into the Army? And the dramatic tale of that
poor boy who couldn't get any working papers because it
turned out he'd never been born? It's just the age-old story
of bureaucracy. For the bureaucrat the only reality is his
archives. If your dossier says you're dead, it's no use to tell
him, 'But I'm standing right here in front of you, alive!'
He'll just answer you by pulling out your dossier and saying,
'You can talk all you want, but it says right here on Line
18b that you are deceased as of last January, and all I can
do is say a prayer for the repose of your soul.' Therefore, if
one manages to find work abroad and needs documents to
get a passport, one can stay here until one dies of hunger. Of
course if you're really dead and your mother has to go to
town hall to get a permit to bury you, the functionary
shakes his head and exclaims, 'These young people today are
so pig-headed. I explained to your daughter at least thirty
times that she was dead!' "

Jo shrugged her shoulders. "The trouble with you is that

you have absolutely no sense of perspective. You shouldn't make jokes about death. Death is a serious thing."

"I'm not making jokes about death but about bureaucracy, which is not a serious thing."

"Your mind is so embittered with politics. You're the kind of person who would ride on a train and if it crashed headlong into another train, you'd die happy because you could say, 'See how this government has messed up the systems of public transportation?'"

"Come on, Jo, I'm not as factious as all that!"

"You're not factious!" she laughed sarcastically. "I've got a good memory, I remember your once writing in the paper that if you were walking down a railroad track and a fellow who belonged to a certain political party that shall remain nameless warned you to get out of the way because a train was coming, you wouldn't move because the worst that could happen was to be run over by the train, but if you listened to the fellow, who knows what might happen."

"Jo, we're not discussing politics now. When you talk about bureaucracy, you're talking about a plague that besets every country in the world. And, when it comes to bureaucracy, you don't have to invent stories. The most grotesque fantasy can't hold a candle to the real and true follies of bureaucracy."

Jo turned to Margherita. "Mrs. Guareschi, doesn't your husband ever talk seriously?"

"Only on the rare occasions when he wants to kid you," Margherita answered.

Some time after the above conversation, Jo went to visit her baby daughter and came back with a face that looked like a summer squall.

"What's wrong?" Margherita asked.

"My mother."

"Is she ill?"

"No, healthy as a hog, but she's been dead for six months."

Jo didn't find it difficult to talk about what had happened. When you came down to hard facts, it was nothing dramatic: Jo's mother received a telephone call from a government functionary and the following conversation resulted.

"Are you Antonietta Tasca widow of Cicon?"

"Yes."

"You were taken to the emergency ward of Parma Hospital where, after two months of intensive care, you died. The Township of Parma has sent us the hospital bill. Since you're not on the poverty roster, being a homeowner, it's your obligation to pay the bill."

"My obligation? But I've never been in Parma Hospital and I've never died, I mean I'm not dead."

"These papers show that presenting a proper identity card, Antonietta Tasca widow of Cicon enjoyed treatment at Parma Hospital and died after two months. This identity card carries your photograph and the number assigned to you when you applied for it. How do you explain this fact?"

"A year ago, when I was in Parma, my purse was stolen. I reported the theft to the police specifying that my purse contained 4,570 lire, a handkerchief, the keys to my house, and my identity card. Obviously the person who copped my bag was a woman that looked like me and was using my identity card."

"Just like a police film, I suppose. Anyhow, even if it

happened that way, it doesn't relieve you of the responsibility of paying your debts. If they steal your car and the thief hits somebody, you're answerable. That woman died in the capacity of Antonietta Tasca widow of Cicon because you allowed her to steal your identity card."

"I allowed nothing of the sort. How can you say that a poor woman like me would ever allow anybody to steal her purse?"

"We're not saying that. What we're saying is that you did not prevent the theft of purse containing document. If one person does not prevent another from effecting a particular action, it signifies that the former person has permitted the action. Society assigns a name to you, and it's your social duty to keep custody of it. If you had kept proper custody of it, it would not have been misused. Therefore, may we please have your payment."

"There are two facts you left out. One: if I'm alive, I can't have died in Parma Hospital and therefore I'm not responsible for any hospital bills. Two: if I'm dead, nobody can force me to pay!"

"According to the legal documents, you died in Parma Hospital. However, as you must be the proprietor of the effects of Antonietta Tasca widow of Cicon, then you must pay in the capacity of heir."

"Never! If I pay as my own heir, then you'll sock me for inheritance taxes too!"

"Then pay as the decedent. Take this bill to window 3, Accounts Receivable. Out of respect for the dead, we will allow you to pay the bill in installments."

At the end of her tale, Jo shouted indignantly, "What do you make of *that!*"

"Jo," I answered smiling, "it's just one of those stories we journalists fish out again and again to spruce up and use as newspaper fillers. Just old jokes."

"Don't you see that my mother has to pay *because* she died in Parma Hospital *because* she's still alive in our village?"

"That's the line that usually appears at the end of the bureaucratic fables you read in newspapers."

The girl was infuriated. "But this story's true! It wasn't in the newspapers!"

"It will be," Margherita reassured her, "and when we all read it together, we'll get a good laugh out of it."

Before she ran to lock herself in her room, Jo roared like a tiger.

Like Madama Butterfly

✴

The situation was becoming more complicated daily, but suddenly the TV cut it short. This provided me with yet another proof of the truly terrifying power of television.

Let me explain that Jo, after bitter disillusionment with the summer replacement shows on TV, gave herself over to mundane things and spent all of her free time at the beach. "It seems she makes quite a hit in her bathing suit," Margherita informed me. "The girl tells me everything; she's already thrown over three lovesick beaus, but I think she's gotten herself trapped by the fourth. He wants to marry her immediately, no questions asked, and take her home with him."

"Margherita," I said, "this is very bad news for us. However, when you consider that Jo (even though it doesn't show, and the child is so young) is an Unwed Mother, I think it's only fair to give her a helping hand. That is, if it's a serious thing."

When questioned about it, Jo said that it was more than serious. "He's young, handsome, I like him, and he has a small business of his own. Unfortunately he's a foreigner."

"That's not important, Jo. The obstacle of different languages is easily gotten around."

"The obstacle doesn't exist because he succeeds in expressing himself very clearly. That fact remains, he's still a foreigner."

"My dear child," I reassured her, "if you like the young man, his nationality doesn't matter. In matters of love, there should be no racial blocks. Think of your daughter instead."

"I *have* thought, and I'm not really sure if I have the right to impose a father on her just because I like him."

Margherita stepped in. "All mothers impose fathers on their children. In fact, it's not customary, before marrying a man, to ask the opinion of the children that will result from this union."

"My case is different," Jo answered. "My little girl is nearly two years old and her natural father is somebody else."

Jo wavered, but it was obvious that her resistance was being worn down more each day. But as we were just beginning to resign ourselves to the loss of Jo, the TV intervened. It was a talk show called *Cordially Yours,* and the emcee was interviewing foreign women married to Italian men. The consensus was that the foreign women were not satisfied with their Italian husbands, and in the main, they said they could barely endure them. Jo was listening attentively to the program and when it was over she observed, "What they were talking about was always marriages where the woman has to take care of mountains of things and put up, like it or not, with the habits and environment of the man. What a gruesome set-up. Tomorrow I'm dumping that foreigner."

"The situations aren't analogous, I don't think," Margherita objected. "They were talking about foreign women marrying Italian men."

"It's my situation exactly," Jo answered. "It's the situation in which women marry men of different race and, therefore, there will always be between those woman and their husbands conflicts of a mental and habitual nature."

"It depends," Margherita said. "This conflict might exist if you were to marry a Japanese, a Congolese, a Chinese, an Indian, or a Turk. But if your young man is, let's say, a Frenchman, a Swiss, a Belgian, an Austrian, a Portuguese, a Dutchman, something along those lines, the difference in your mentalities and habits would be practically minimal."

"This I know perfectly well," Jo answered. "The fact is, my suitor happens to be from Apulia."

Margherita was indignant. "But then if he's Italian there's no problem at all!"

"On the contrary, it's doubly problematic," the girl explained. "Because, besides being a foreigner, he's also an Italian. You saw what a pitiful showing Italian husbands make. No, there's no doubt in my mind: either I marry somebody from Emilia like me, or, if I have to fall back on somebody from another country, I'll marry a Frenchman, a Belgian, a Finn, a Hungarian, a Peruvian, or something of the sort. Anyhow, as of this moment I'm not marrying anybody because, apart from everything else, rather than becoming a slave in my own house, I prefer to stay free in somebody else's house."

The last part of her speech was the only part of it that made any sense, and we decided to listen only to that part which, apart from everything else, made us extraordinarily happy.

Jo, dressed fit to kill, went off to a moonlight dance, and once we were alone Margherita said to me: "Giovanni, I'm sure that your sense of honesty will force you to give up your silly condemnation of TV. We owe to TV the fact that Jo isn't leaving us."

"Not at all, Margherita," I said positively. "It only goes to show that I was right and that TV exercises a terrifying influence on disadvantaged persons. I'm afraid I'll have to stick with my original position on the subject."

Margherita shook her head sadly. "Giovanni," she said, "I'm afraid for you. You're on the path to ruination."

Margherita's words worried me. Margherita hasn't had the easiest life, living with me. She's accompanied me, step by step, without an instant of uncertainty or despair, in my long, laborious struggle for a place in the Milanese sun. In February 1942 I announced in a loud voice to the neighborhood at large what I thought about the situation at that point. The night after, they came to arrest me and Margherita advised me simply not to lose my temper. She tore her hair out in the middle of Milan and finally, after finding the proper person, she came to fetch me out of the security cell I was in and took me home. Shortly after that, I was called to arms and Margherita came with me to the train smiling. She said to me, "I'll see you soon."

I came home in poor shape a few months later, and Margherita, who had to fight hard because of the evacuation, food rationing, and Passionaria's being en route to this world, somehow cured me. She came with me to the station again after I pulled myself together and had to return to the regiment. She said simply not to think about things at home, because she was all that was needed to manage little Albertino and finish the construction of Passionaria.

A week later, on September 9, 1943, I went via cattle car

to a concentration camp in Poland. I came home exactly two years later, in September of 1945, agile as a gazelle and with a marvelous mustache. I weighed forty-six kilos. But Margherita, who was even thinner than I was, congratulated me on how well I looked. Then we faced the battle to get our apartment and my job back. From '45 to '48 the air was pretty hot and I threw myself bodily into the political battle. This was no bed of roses. Margherita has always read my correspondence (she is fully entitled to), and none of the threats and frightening talk in the hundreds of them I received in those years ever seemed to disturb her.

Then I fell into a defamation suit and lost the case. Margherita, without tears or sighs, helped me fill up my stalag ditty bag and took me over to the prison. There I remained for thirteen months, and every fifteen days Margherita came to visit me along with the two children, never seeming discouraged or worried. Then I came home again and more large and small troubles followed, finding Margherita always serene and peaceful, and we eventually solved all the problems that came along.

It's because of all this that when Margherita said very worriedly that she thought I was on the wrong path and was afraid for me, it left me somewhat perplexed.

Margherita can play only one sport—reading my correspondence. This is nothing new, as I said before, and it's never bothered me because it's not a question of curiosity or jealousy; it's simply the activity of a sportswoman, a kind of intellectual athletics. This makes her up-to-date on what my fans write in reaction to what I say when I dare talk about the idols created by TV.

"Giovanni, you're living in a world of your own. Can't you

see that pop singers have become the most important thing
in Italy today? Aren't you aware of the fierce love millions
of Italians have for their favorite stars? Doesn't it frighten
you at all, the hate and distaste that ooze out of the protest
letters you receive? In the end, what difference do these
singers and stars make, anyway? Why don't you leave them
alone?"

"I'm not after the stars, Margherita. What I'm fighting is
adulation of stars, making them an 'ism.' I'm not against
stardom—singers and actors are doing a job and if they're
stars, usually it means they're doing their job well. What I'm
violently against is the new religion TV has spawned, the
worship of stars, 'Milva-ism' for example."

"I understand perfectly, Giovanni, but clearly you're not
getting through with what you're writing."

Margherita is always right. I have in front of me a letter
from a sixteen-year-old girl who lives in Monza. It begins:
"I'm a Milva-ist." Farther on she says: "You're out of your
mind, saying you've 'got nothing against Milva' but you
'simply object to Milva-ism.' Would you please explain to
me what you mean by Milva-ism? Turn your mind back a few
years to 30 A.D. and think about bumping into somebody
who says to you, 'I'm not against Jesus Christ, I just hate
Christianity.' "

That's the crux of the issue, right there. The pop singer
apotheosized. His gestures, his shouting, his lyrics taken as a
religion. These sixteen-year-olds who howl, sigh, and roll
around on the ground in front of a singer, don't they go back
to horrible scenes of pagan idolatry, where, to the relentless
beat of a drum, maenads furiously reveled around their
wooden idols exciting themselves to the point of cutting open

their stomachs with a knife or dancing frantically on red-hot coals?

"Margherita, who if not television has created this unlimited power, this divinity, this religion, this horde of fanatics?"

"These TV stars too shall pass!"

"Sure, but star-worship will remain. And even if the years go by there will always be teeny-boppers. Because, along with everything else, TV has created teeny-bopperism. In our day, sixteen-year-olds were graceful, charming children about to come out of adolescence. There wasn't a special problem involving sixteen-year-olds. Now, thanks to TV, sixteen-year-olds (which constitutes the category of people between the ages of fourteen and twenty-one) are at the forefront and loaded with 'basic problems.' They set themselves up as judges of their parents and of the entire human race, and they go merrily on their way to conquering the right to be called a plague."

Margherita shook her head. "Giovanni, you belong to another age. These sixteen-year-olds belong to the future. If they can't and don't even care to interfere with your past, why do you want to interfere with their future?"

"It's a question of sentimentality. After having spent such a long time to cultivate our little garden, to fill it up, to clean out the weeds, it's sad to have to leave it to the ravages of a plague of locusts."

Margherita shook her head for the umpteenth time. "Let them. What good is your garden if babies don't come out of cabbages any more?"

Jo came in and announced that she had liquidated her lovesick swain. That bit of news consoled us.

Marriage for Love

☼

Jo happened to watch with Margherita one night an interesting documentary on the Italian-Swiss network about Swedish Unwed Mothers. She was very impressed with it, and as soon as I was within earshot she began to share her enthusiasm with me.

"For one thing," she said, "in Sweden they don't call them 'unwed mothers,' they say 'maternity singles.' In addition, in spite of not being married, the maternity single is entitled by law to call herself 'Mrs.' Furthermore, the fathers of the child have to pay the maternity single a fixed sum every month for maintenance of the child. Even if the father of the child is married."

"The father*s*?" I said suspiciously. "I'd always heard that a child can't have more than one father."

"Shows how much you know," Jo snorted. "What if the girl was having relations with two or three men at the same time? How do you decide whether the father is the first, second, or third? The law takes this into consideration."

"I see," I said, "each of the possible fathers pays one third."

"Not at all!" the girl exclaimed. "Since a child for technical reasons can only have one father, why should the other two have to pay? When she's questioned by the authorities, the girl designates one of the men as the child's father. That's the one who pays. Then, when the child is old enough, they give him blood tests and other things and if it turns out that the blood type and other things don't match the putative father, they reimburse the fellow and the girl indicates Potential Culprit No. 2. If the tests show he's the father of the child, he picks up the tab. If not, we go to the third man. If your potential fathers are five or six in number, you keep on going like this till you find the right one. Also, the State gives the maternity single subsidies and a job, but the most important advantage is that a maternity single can get an apartment immediately, but legally married people have to wait for seven years to get one. Isn't this the height of civilization?"

"I guess so," Margherita said without too much conviction.

"There you have the typical attitude of the Married Mother!" the girl exclaimed. "Isn't the function of women in society to bring children into the world and raise them? Well then, what difference does it make if a woman has children by her own husband or by somebody else's? According to you, is it fair if after I've paid my debt to society by giving it a child, I should get the raw end of the deal just because I'm an unwed mother, while that dirty rat of a celibate father doesn't chip in a lira? Is it fair to deny me even the small satisfaction of being called 'Mrs.'? If I'm unwed, does it mean I'm any less a mother than a Married Mother?"

"Not really," I said. "Perhaps you're more a mother

because you raise your child with your own two hands. Jo, from now on we will call you 'Mrs.' "

"I wasn't talking about the two of you," the girl answered. "If you only knew what I have to go through when I go home and run into the usual clutch of old matrons who smile like vultures and say, 'Why hello there, Miss Cicon! And your little girl, how is she, Miss Cicon?' If you only knew how much I'd like to go back there with a husband the size of a mountain and half a kilo of diamonds on my finger."

A few days after this exchange of opinions, Jo rushed into the breakfast room, very upset.

"*He*'s here!"

"Who's *he?*"

"*Him.* The Unwed Father of the child! He says he has to talk to me. What am I going to do?"

"Ask him in and let him talk," Margherita said, getting up. "You can talk to him here. We'll leave."

"I'll see him here, but the two of you stay! I'm terrified—terrified that I'll smash his head in."

In her right hand she was squeezing a heavy meat mallet and she showed every intention of using it. She was a poor girl all alone in the world, painfully aware of her own weaknesses. I told her to ask the fellow in.

He turned out to be a big hulk about twenty-three years old, rather well dressed and nicely turned out. He didn't have any trouble expressing himself in our presence.

"Jo," he said, "I'm here to give a name to our daughter."

"Mine suits her perfectly well," Jo answered.

"Her mother's husband's would suit her better."

"Look, you've already tried once to get me to marry you," Jo said coldly. "And I told you then that, apart from all other considerations, I'm not the type to marry Army rejects."

"That's nonsense, Jo," I inserted. "If a man isn't fit for military service, he might be eminently suited to marriage."

"Exactly," the young man agreed. "In any case, I was never classified 4-F, just 2-A. Every time I get a draft notice, they tell me after the physical that I'm 2-A. It's just a question of finding the right fellow to take your bribe. I found the right fellow. The trouble is so did everybody else and now the whole set-up is blown sky-high and the guy was discharged. Now they've gotten really tight and since I'm unfortunately bursting with health, they're sure to catch me this time around."

"Good," Jo said approvingly. "You go behave like a soldier, and then, after I've seen you in your Alpine Corps uniform, maybe I'll change my mind and marry you."

The young man shook his head. "Jo, why do you want me to throw away fifteen months of my life? Now they've made a sensible law exempting young married fathers with at least one child. Since we have a daughter, all we have to do is get married and I can stay home very peacefully."

I glanced at the knuckles of Jo's hand, which had gone white as she squeezed the meat mallet tighter and tighter. I got ready to grab her. Instead she suddenly let go of the mallet and dropped it on the chair.

"I see," she exclaimed. "A Marriage of Love."

The young man shrugged his shoulders. "You have to be practical in this life," he explained. "You're a young girl and rather pretty, you're the mother of my daughter, you're a worker; why shouldn't I want to marry you when there are so many advantages?"

"I see," said Jo. "Except one of those advantages has to be you doing your military service. You do your bit for fifteen months and then we'll talk about it again."

"But what you're saying makes no sense!" the young man protested indignantly. "There are those who avoid military service by chopping a hand off with an ax or sticking their foot under a streetcar wheel. I'm going even farther than that, I'm inviting marriage. Isn't that enough of a sacrifice?"

"Nothing compared to mine if I married you!" Jo retorted. "I'm not so patriotic as to give up my personal liberty to prevent the Italian army from enlisting a bad soldier."

"Jo," the young man persisted, "we're living in the space age and we can always make an arrangement. I'll go on about my business, and you go on about yours, without interference, and if there are money problems, I'd be glad to give you a monthly stipend . . ."

Jo picked up the meat mallet again. "If I didn't have a child," she said coldly, "I'd make your head into a veal cutlet. I think I'd better go back to the kitchen."

It was a good idea and we let her go. Once she had left the room, the young man spread his arms wide. "The girl has no principles," he wailed. "And her mother is worse than she is. Would you believe it, yesterday I went to talk to her about it and she told me that if her daughter marries me, she'll never speak to her again?"

"I believe it," I said. "The answer is to stop this theatrical nonsense. Life in the Army isn't hell, you know. A lot of young men find it rather amusing."

"But how can I stay away from home for fifteen months now that I've finally found the woman that's perfect for me? I'm not talking about Jo, you understand."

"Well then, marry *her!*" Margherita exclaimed.

"She's already married, damn it! I don't know where to turn next. Don't you have any suggestions for me?"

"Given your situation, you could latch on to another unwed mother," Margherita said. "We have an unwed mother right here in town whom you could marry with little difficulty to give her son a name. She's not yet fifty and her baby's a very handsome twenty-one-year-old boy."

The young man thought about it seriously and then shook his head. "It wouldn't work. The son can avoid the draft as an only son of a widowed mother. Once he has a father, he'd have to do his military service, so he'd never let his mother get married. There's no escape!"

"There's nothing left but to declare yourself a conscientious objector," I concluded.

"He can't," Jo said firmly as she came back into the room like a storm cloud. "He doesn't have a conscience." She was squeezing the handle of her meat mallet tightly and the young man left on the run, taking his worries with him.

Ladies and Gentlemen

When I was a boy, in the Valley we only danced at the village carnival. The "Festival" would come, a traveling dance hall. They would spread out a nice parquet-panel dance floor over the grass of a field; around the pavement they erected a grandstand on three sides, and on the front side a vast façade decorated in wild colors with two entry gates and between them the two ticket windows. Above one of the doors the word MEN was written, over the other WOMEN, and the two ticket windows had similar, smaller signs—the entrances were separate because the entry fee for men was higher than for women. The latter were divided into two categories: women and chaperones. The chaperones were old ladies who brought girls to the dance and didn't pay an entry fee. There were special benches on the sidelines for the old ladies. At the far end of the Festival tent there was a bandstand packed with every conceivable brass instrument plus a bull fiddle and a drum. Dead center were the tent poles which held up the white dome of the tent.

The Festival had a poetry of its own, not the least of which was the prelude to the ball, the "invitational" ceremony. The band arrayed itself in front of the inn on the square and played the piece that was *de rigeur,* an infernal waltz called *The Nightingale,* minus the clarinetist who would hie himself up to the belfry if the parish priest let him, or if not, to the window of the tallest house in the square. When the band reached a certain point in the piece, the clarinet chimed in from on high with a formidable descant and solo of myriad chromatic runs, a cascade of trills designed to make a nightingale expire with jealousy.

Then, those monstrosities called amplifiers and microphones, which allow people who are totally voiceless or afflicted with chronic laryngitis to become world-famous stars, were still a mere gleam in God's eye. In those days, in order to be a singer you had to sing. And to create a sensation, you sent the clarinetist up to the belfry.

We still have some of those Festival tents touring around the countryside. But now they're called "Dancing" and they don't have poles in the middle any more to hold up the tent but are made of sheet plastic held up by metal arcades. Inside, there are little tables and a bar. No more benches for the Old Ladies. The Old Ladies either stay at home watching TV or sneak in to dance disguised as kids. Brass bands don't exist any more; they've been replaced by Rock combos with amplifiers and screamers instead of singers.

What I'm driving at is that, while she lived in the country, our domestic assistant Jo wasn't lacking for spiritual food. Thus it happened that, after frequenting the Dancing in town for quite a while without any visible consequences, Jo began coming home from the dance very worried-looking and spent long hours locked in her room.

"She's in love," Margherita decided.

This went on for more than a month but finally one night

Jo came home from the dance with a new light in her eyes. "It's all working out perfectly," she told us. "I'll win yet!"

"Wonderful," Margherita answered. "Watch out you don't miss any tricks."

"I won't, don't worry!" she said confidently. "Thursday's a holiday and they'll be dancing in the afternoon. You ought to come over and see for yourselves. I want to hear what you think!"

I said that we would rather die than set foot in that nuthouse, and she answered, "I see. You can't stand to see other people if they're still young and lively."

"Not at all, Jo. I can't stand my being so old. It's also a question of esthetics. An old man among boys stands out like a turnip in a bouquet of roses."

"Ridiculous! You should see some of the fossils that turn up at the Dancing."

"I'm sure of it, Jo—but this only happens because there are people who won't grow old gracefully. Too many people go too far both ways. Either they give up the ghost and unnecessarily become decrepit, or they behave as if they were still sixteen. With the result that, in the first instance, you feel pity, and in the second, you laugh."

We shelved the issue until Margherita and I were alone together. Then she said, "Jo is a girl with a lot of common sense. She made one mistake and for fear of making a second mistake she's asking our advice. We've followed her arduous spiritual struggle and we can't abandon her now."

"How can you give advice when it comes to love?" I exclaimed.

"All we're called upon to do is to show our interest in her sentimental problems."

Thursday finally arrived and we went to the Dancing with Jo. There wasn't the mob I expected in the huge room and you could actually breathe the air. We took up our stations at a little table and began to keep an eye on Jo. Very shortly we saw her engrossed in dancing with a young man with long hair and very tight pants. "Dancing *with*" is an exaggeration; each of the two of them was doing his own thing, and one minute they were facing each other, another side by side, and the next back to back. Their chief preoccupation seemed to be to avoid touching each other.

At a certain point the young man disappeared and Jo kept the dance up by herself. I'm no dance critic, being limited myself to the waltz, the tango, and the fox trot, so I'm in no position to describe the dance Jo was doing. But since all of my readers have doubtless seen a pneumatic drill at work, I can tell you that the girl's dance was like a pneumatic drill with two attractive legs in place of the usual steel chisel.

But that's irrelevant.

We looked around for the young man and discovered him, after the dance was over, sitting at a little table and chatting calmly with two other fellows.

"They must have had a fight," Margherita said. "In a fit of pique he left her standing on the dance floor, and she didn't want to give him satisfaction, so she went on dancing as if to say she couldn't care less. It's a good tactic; in this case the girl has the style of dancing on her side. But if it had been a tango or a waltz, how could she have gone on dancing by herself?"

The dance was over and Jo came back to sit with us.

"Well?" she said. "What do you think?"

"The fellow seemed interesting," Margherita said tactfully.

"What fellow?"

"The fellow you were dancing with."

"Maybe so," the girl said. "But he doesn't interest *me*."

"I see," Margherita said. "You've thrown him over. I saw him go off to sit with his friends."

"Obviously he was tired," Jo said. "That's his business. So tell me what you think."

"To tell the truth," Margherita said, "a gentleman who leaves a lady in the middle of the dance floor and goes off to sit with his friends isn't my idea of very nice."

Jo gaped with astonishment at Margherita. "Mrs. Guareschi, since when were we talking about ladies and gentlemen?"

"All along," Margherita said irritably. "Since you were dancing as a couple, that made him the gentleman and you the lady."

"Ooooogh," the girl said, giggling hysterically. "Me the lady and that gorilla a *gentleman?*"

"I wouldn't say gorilla," Margherita defended him. "If he had a decent haircut and pants that weren't three sizes too small for him, he'd be a handsome boy."

"Mrs. Guareschi!" the girl said coldly. "I've already said that boy doesn't interest me. I don't even know his name or where he comes from. Now let's drop the subject and talk about something else."

"What else shall we talk about?" Margherita asked.

"Me, of course. That's why I asked you to come over here. Does it seem to you as if I've finally been able to get the hang of the thing?"

"What thing?"

"The Shake! I've been working on it for a month, even at home. I want your objective opinion about how I do the Shake!"

"To tell the truth," I stammered, "we couldn't follow it very well."

"Listen, they're playing another Shake," Jo exclaimed, getting up. "Now watch me closely."

"Aren't you going to wait for somebody to ask you to dance?" Margherita asked, astounded.

"Why? Didn't I pay for the ticket myself? I'll dance when it suits me to."

She walked confidently onto the dance floor and began to dance by herself. All the other young people were doing the same thing. No couples, but rather a collective dance, en masse.

"Giovanni," Margherita said indignantly, "do you realize we've come to a point in history where young people actually go to a dance hall to *dance?* A dance isn't what it was in our day, a nice time to meet people, talk, get to know one another."

"A dance isn't to get to know one another any more," I said. "When a boy likes a girl, he tells her so wherever he happens to run into her. The girl does the same thing if she decides she likes some boy. You don't talk and you don't kid around. Dancing is a very serious thing with these young people today."

We looked at Jo. She went on gyrating and shimmying with all her concentration and a lot of style, and when she came back to the table, we said to her, "Jo, if this Shake can be called a dance, you do it better than all the other girls."

"I'm glad," she said, very pleased with herself. "But of course you think these dances are something out of an insane asylum."

"No, that would be like saying that moving to the sound of music belongs only in an insane asylum. But for thousands of years, people haven't felt that way. How you move to the sound of music doesn't matter."

"Now wait a minute," Jo complained. "I didn't ask you to come here just to have you tell me that kids are nothing but unchained maniacs."

"We were maniacs in one way, the young people today are maniacs in another," I answered.

"I don't understand," Jo growled, "but it must be a philosophical concept. Do you want to try dancing the Shake with me?"

"I'd be glad to," I said. "But I'll follow the example of the first partner we saw: you dance and I'll stay sitting here while I finish my drink."

"Wonderful," Margherita exclaimed. "And I'll stay here and dance the Shake with that young fellow in the black turtleneck who's working out over there in the corner."

"You've chosen the wrong gentleman, Mrs. Guareschi," said Jo. "That boy in the turtleneck happens to be a girl."

"Oh dear," Margherita said sadly, "these modern dances aren't made for us refugees from another century."

Jo's Nose

When is a person truly happy?"

I was intent on creating suggestive fire pictures by pushing the huge elmwood log burning in the fireplace with the poker, and Jo's voice gave me a start.

"I don't know."

"That's nice!" the girl retorted. "Older than God and you still don't know when a person is happy. Haven't you ever been happy in your life?"

"No, I never tried to be."

"I see. You've led an unhappy, gloomy, sad life."

"Quite the contrary. I simply found that I had to walk down a certain path wearing a pair of good shoes that happened to be too narrow. But from time to time I would sit on the curb, take off my shoes and socks, cool my feet in the stream running alongside, and then walk on barefoot. Over the years, the shoes got used to the feet and now they're pretty shoddy, but they're comfortable."

"I see your philosophy!" our domestic assistant exclaimed. "What you're saying is that you were happy when you took off your tight shoes. In other words, happiness is the cessation of unhappiness."

"No. How can a man be happy walking barefoot on a stony path? How can a man be happy who has a tooth pulled after a week of pain? He may not have the pain any more, but he's lost a tooth."

Jo is an intelligent girl and she's shown it by leaving her job at a stinking glue factory to come and work as a domestic assistant. ("Better than working for that reeking machine is to work for two senile fossils—less work, more pay!")

"In other words, you've never been happy because you didn't know for sure what you wanted from life."

"Not at all! I knew exactly the things I wanted, and I got them all. The trouble is, I was never sure that those things were really important enough to bring happiness."

Margherita stopped working on the famous dark-green pullover for a minute and said authoritatively, "There are three ingredients to happiness: to be a fool, to be selfish, and to be healthy. If you don't have the first ingredient, all is lost."

"You're cynical, Margherita," I said.

"Not me, Flaubert," she answered.

Jo looked at her with new respect, but Margherita explained. "Once upon a time there was more reverence and love for culture. Even the people who couldn't study the classics succeeded in learning a sackful of important things thanks to the fact that, hidden inside your chocolate teardrops there were little pieces of paper with maxims quoted from great men of culture, art, politics, and so on. That way usefulness was united with pleasure. I learned that maxim about happiness from a chocolate teardrop."

Jo sighed with disillusion and then said, "The fact remains, I'm profoundly unhappy."

"Jo," Margherita said in a motherly tone, "don't let yourself be led down the garden path by the glossies or TV where they talk about happiness and unhappiness with unscrupulous frivolity. Don't confuse unhappiness, which is a terrible thing, with an insignificant, passing annoyance."

"I'm still unhappy," Jo repeated. "I've been unhappy for years and I will be for the rest of my life if I don't find the courage to act. I hate myself! Understand? I hate myself! In the morning when I look in the mirror to comb my hair I almost feel like spitting in my face."

"That's nothing," said Margherita. "We'll just change the mirror in your bathroom. That must be the problem, because I can't see anything in your face to explain self-hatred."

"No!" Jo shouted. "There's nothing wrong with the mirror. I have to change my face! But look, does it seem fair to you that I have to have a nose like this?"

"Certainly," Margherita said. "It's the only nose you can have—it's *your* nose."

"It's *not* mine! My nose is a little French snub, a cute unconventional pixie-type nose, slightly ski-jump."

"Be reasonable!" Margherita said. "How can a French nose sit in the middle of an Italian, much less an Emilian, face?"

The girl wrung her hands and wailed. "But can't you see how I'm suffering? Mrs. Guareschi, I've been unhappy too long and I have the sacred right to some happiness for myself. Can't you understand that I can't wear this horrible nose any more?"

It was time for my ancient, wise voice to be heard. "Jo, that's the nose that God gave you and the nose you must have. Instead of looking at your own nose all the time, why don't you look around at other people's?"

"Because I'm condemned to wear my nose, not other people's. And I've worn it long enough. Tomorrow I'm going to Milan and have my nose changed!"

"I see," I said. "I saw that repulsive TV program about plastic surgery for noses too. But I never dreamed it could arouse the fantasies of a normal girl."

"I'm not a normal girl! I'm plagued by a rhinoceros complex!"

"What's the rhinoceros got to do with it?"

"Why does the rhinoceros become fierce and vicious when people stop to look at him? Because he thinks everybody is making fun of that idiotic object that is supposed to be his nose. So he charges his molesters both to get even with them and in the secret hope that he'll break his nose. So don't knock plastic surgery!"

"I'm not 'knocking' plastic surgery," I protested. "Plastic surgery is a very serious, admirable branch of medicine when it is used to repair damages or dreadful congenital defects that will embitter a person's life. But when it's used on silly little girls who want to change their profiles without any sensible reason at all, then it's not a branch of medicine any longer. And it should be prosecuted by law because it changes a person's most distinctive feature. This seems a real crime to me. In fact, since we're talking about a mentally underdeveloped person, the punishment should be doubly severe; the same as for child molesting."

"I'm not underdeveloped, mentally or otherwise, and I'm

going to Milan to have my nose fixed. So I want a week's vacation. I've saved up the money and that's the essential thing."

"No," I said warningly. "You will have to get your mother's permission in writing for the doctor to perform the operation."

"Where did my mother come into this? It's *my* nose!"

"Yes, Jo, but it's as underage as you are. So go to your mother, come back with her legal permission, show it to me, and I'll let you make the trip to Milan."

"Okay," the girl said. "Now I want your honest opinion. Let's see if you like what I've picked out. Look at these and tell me which nose you find most attractive."

She spread out a huge sheet covered with photographs, some real and some cut out of magazines. Margherita moved over to look at the photographs but I refused indignantly. "Jo, I simply cannot understand why you want a nose like Elizabeth Taylor's or Belinda Lee's or Gina Lollobrigida's, when you've got one of your very own that doesn't have any pertinent defects."

"It has the worst defect of all!" the girl howled. "I hate it!"

Margherita quickly examined the pictures and handed one of them to Jo. "Here. This is the nose I like best."

"But it's a picture of me!" the girl objected.

"I hadn't noticed, actually," Margherita said. "In any case, it's the nose that suits you best."

Our domestic assistant lost her temper. "You all think like mummies!" she shouted. "You're avoiding the issue because you can't stand the idea of my being happy! But why should I care? My mother isn't a decrepit bourgeois

like the two of you and she'll understand. The bourgeoisie is
passé! The future belongs to the proletariat!"

She took off in the car at three in the afternoon. By the
time she came back that night the fog had set in. None of
you can imagine what the fog in our Valley is like. If the
Lombards say you can cut their fog with a knife, our Valley
fog can only be cut with a woodsman's saw. If you try to
motor in it, you're liable to find yourself in a ditch or
wrapped around a tree. So there was nothing strange about
the scratches and bandages on Jo's face.

"Where'd you have the accident?" I asked.

"In the kitchen," Jo answered gloomily. "My mother was
making some pastry; when I told her about the permission
she started to hit me with the rolling pin. She wanted to
break my head! Instead she smashed my nose. Do you
realize? She smashed my nose! She evidently broke something. I had to go to the doctor to have it set."

Margherita is a sentimental woman, and her eyes filled
with tears. A sob shook her.

"Margherita, don't be upset," I said kindly. "She can't
have hit her very hard. With those arms she surely would
have knocked Jo's head off, if she'd hit her full force."

"I know, I know," Margherita sobbed. "It's just that
these old-fashioned mothers have a sort of ingenuous spon-
taneity that is so touching!"

Jo was furious. "If my mother thinks she's going to have
her way about it, she's wrong!" she shouted.

"Yes," I said. "But honestly you should admit that we
were right in saying that's your nose. You'll feel it when the
swelling sets in."

"It'll heal and as sood as it does, I'b leavigg for Milad!" she shrieked nasally.

It healed, but Jo didn't go to Milan. When the bandages came off Jo's nose had lost the tiny bump that had upset her so much. And even though it still wasn't a French pixie snub it was a pleasant nose to see and wear.

Such is the power of motherly love.

Sexual Education

✵

Jo is a modern girl, but she still has, as we do, those "dead corners" in her mind that seem to evade the beneficent light of Progress and progressivism. So from time to time there are little flare-ups that can be terribly disconcerting.

"Hey," she shouted one day, waving a highly respected newspaper under my nose, "have you read this junk?"

"No, and I don't intend to."

"Well then, I'll tell you about it," the girl answered. "This Milanese mama is waiting for her second child to pop out. She reads that sincere sexual education is highly recommended by leading newspapers and magazines. So she calls her eight-year-old, whom they describe here as 'awake and a born observer,' and explains to him, 'gracefully and delicately,' what is happening to her."

" 'Gracefully and delicately' in what sense?" Margherita put in.

"The Milanese mama doesn't tell you in her letter to the paper. It's my guess it went something like this: 'Pierino, do you know why mummie's tummy is swelling up like this?' 'Because mummie obviously ate too much English stew, which isn't good for the tummy.' 'No, Pierino. Mummie's tummy is swelling up because inside, your little brother is growing bigger every day!' 'Oh my,' says Pierino, 'how did he get inside?' At this point undoubtedly our Milanese mama 'gracefully and delicately' told the boy everything, with proper emphasis on the husband's role in the phenomenon. 'Aow, then it's not the stork that brings babies!' poor Pierino decides. 'Stork?' says the mama in disgust. 'Only stupid children believe in the stork. Babies are born the way I told you, Pierino. Do you understand?' 'Oh, yes, mummie. So if my friend Rosina and I want a baby, we could make one too!' 'No, no, Pierino! First you'd have to get married!' 'But why, mummie? Ninetta, the concierge's daughter, has a baby, and she's not married!' 'Yes, Pierino, but that's not nice. Anyway it's for grown-ups to do, not children!' 'But mummie, Ninetta was only thirteen when her baby came!' And so forth and so on. Something along those lines, given the fact that the boy is 'awake and a born observer.' "

"I believe you," Margherita said. "But what I don't understand is why something like this was published in the newspaper."

"Very simple," Jo explained, "because the tiny tot, the very next morning, told all his schoolmates, boys and girls, just how babies are born. So the little girls and boys took the news home with them and their mummies didn't like it at all and started treating the modern mummie like a 'half-criminal,' as she puts it."

"Quite right," Margherita commented. "I hope the editorial note promotes her to full criminal."

"On the contrary!" the girl exclaimed. "And that's what made me so upset. The editor writes that the Milanese mama behaved perfectly and she did exactly the right thing. The only complaint the editor has is that mummie should have told Pierino not to let the cat out of the bag with his school chums, because there are these backward parents who 'prefer to tell their children stories about storks, cabbages, stores where you buy newborn babies, just as when they were younger, children were told that the infant Jesus brought them Christmas gifts.' It goes on in the same vein."

Margherita spread out her arms. "If that's the case," she said, "then that prestigious newspaper indirectly accuses Giovanni and me of being bad parents, and we can only bow our heads in shame."

I rebelled against this. "That prestigious newspaper of yours is full of sawdust!" I shouted. "We were *not* bad parents. The bad parents are these modern mamas and papas who are robbing their children of the best part of their lives. They're dreadful parents because they pay attention to these crypto-pornographic articles instead of honestly asking themselves what the point is of telling a child between the ages of five and twelve about the technical aspects of reproduction. If they'd just ask themselves that question maybe the only possible answer would pop into their minds: the senseless result is that an instinct that exists in every living thing and manifests itself when nature tells it to will be prematurely awakened in the child.

"A few weeks ago I saw a monstrous article in a magazine about a mother and father who found a way to teach their children to read at the age of two or three. The disgraceful parents announced that at that age the mind is 'free, tender, receptivity is at a maximum, and the child registers everything with extreme ease.' This way children 'gain time.'

Actually, with this system, instead of 'registering' those ideas and sensations that are essential to spiritual formation, the child 'registers' trite, cold, technical notions.

"I know that our most famous educators have completed thorough studies and ponderous dissertations to show how you can force a child of two, three, and four years old to learn things that formerly they only began to learn at the age of six. I know all this, but it doesn't stop me from saying I think formal education should be put off until the age of ten. I can't believe that children should be brought up like chickens, in batteries of cells. From a purely economic point of view, it's marvelous that they can grow chickens that weigh a kilo in one short month. But think how they do it: by imprisoning the chicks in narrow cages where they can't use up energy or fat by moving around, and feeding them with scientific-formula mush. You don't get chickens out of those cells; you get flaccid, spongy, tasteless pap.

"Do you know that these chicken factories actually have a machine to collect the droppings and process them to recover any material that might still have food value? So that's why I'll eat without complaint the toughest barnyard cock, instead of those pre-digested puddings that are factory-reared chickens. And long live old-fashioned mothers! It's a sin to steal childhood from children. Instead, it should be prolonged as much as possible. For a healthy, strong plant to grow properly it needs fine, deep roots, and our childhood and dreams and the stories we were told are the roots of our lives. If I was able to endure troubles of all kinds without losing courage, and if I can still work with childlike enthusiasm, I owe this ability to the precious gift my parents gave me—a long, clean childhood full of fables and dreams.

"In moments of hard fighting, of need, of fear, of hunger, of sickness, of bitterness, when the old trunk of my tree withers and the branches dry up and fall down, my roots, tightly clinging to the earth, seem somehow to be able to suck up the life juice to keep the tree alive.

"During the worst part of the storm, I always find one certain haven—my long childhood with its dreams and fairy tales. I'm sixty years old and I know a thing or two. But in spite of every logical argument I still refuse to admit that the shoe I put on the kitchen windowsill the night before St. Lucy's day was filled by my mother and not St. Lucy on her flying donkey. I'm positive it was filled by St. Lucy! I'm ashamed to remember the time, many years ago when Albertino was just thirteen—when we had just finished our traditional dinner on Christmas Eve, I brought the presents downstairs to distribute them personally instead of sneaking them under the tree the way I'd always done before. It embarrasses me to think how furious Albertino was. To this day I can't understand why he didn't call me an idiot. I deserved it—"

"Well, *I* called you an idiot," Margherita reminded me with justifiable pride.

"Then you don't agree with the newspaper either," Jo said.

"Of course I don't," I answered. "What the newspaper says isn't true at all: 'Stories about storks and cabbages are so handy.' They're not handy at all; it's much more difficult to try to prolong childhood than it is to shorten it by disabusing children of their notions and brutally pushing them into reality, which is ugly and hard."

"But why," said Margherita, "do the newspapers and TV

and the movies insist on the need for disillusioning children and forcing them to face reality from the earliest years, beginning with this business of sex?"

"Because it follows right along with the selfish desire of most parents who, having brought children into the world and nourished them with vain hopes for their first two or three years, have only one wish left—to get the children off their hands, out from underfoot. And of course, since the papers and TV and movies are very commercial, they try to please their clientele. These tribes who tour from place to place to the rhythm of Rock music are one consequence of this selfishness on the part of modern parents, who make their children grow up too soon to get them out of the house. That's the whole story and it's logical for a child to search the outside world for what he can't find at home, so they get married at sixteen and seventeen. Once they're seventeen, they feel tired and worn out and disillusioned. This is why Margherita and I still feel responsible for our children even though they now have children of their own."

At this point Jo said: "What would you have said to the Milanese mama who was complaining to the newspaper because the other children's mothers treated her like a 'half-criminal'?"

"I would have answered: Madame, you're right to complain. Those mothers were wrong to treat you like a 'half-criminal.' They should have treated you like a 'whole fool.' "

Jo approved. "I like you," she said to me, "because you always say things so gracefully and with such a fine ear for metaphor."

At War with Witches

It was a clear October night and for some time now Ful had been baying like a lost soul.

"Let's go see why he's making such a racket," I said to Michelone.

We went out into the courtyard and the mystery was solved right away.

"He's baying at the moon," I explained to Michelone.

"Why?" Michelone asked.

Michelone is not the type to be satisfied with evasive explanations. On the other hand, it's not easy to explain to a two-and-a-half-year-old child why dogs bay at the moon. All I know about the moon is that it has certain marked effects on oceans, on the decanting and bottling of wine, and things of that sort. So I said I simply didn't know.

Michelone glanced up and found the perfect explanation. "Ful's crying because the moon is broken."

Indeed, a chunk of it was missing, and I was very proud of Michelone's acute powers of observation. "Quite right. Ful is crying because the moon is broken."

Naturally the story didn't end at that. Michelone tugged at my sleeve and said, "Who broke it?"

So I answered, "It was broken by planes that fly way up there and shake houses with their terrible roars." The explanation seemed to satisfy him, and we went back inside. Once we were in the breakfast room, however, this tiny prodigy was struck by a worrisome thought: "When a plane goes boom, is the donkey afraid?"

"No," I said confidently.

Reassured, Michelone dived into the closet and emerged with a breadbasket in his hands. He explained that the donkey would be hungry and therefore he must leave a basket for him, filled with breadcrumbs, cubes of sugar, and bran.

Jo started to laugh. "Now how is the donkey going to make it up to your windowsill? The donkey's teeny-tiny and your window is way way up!"

Michelone looked at her as if she were short on brains. "Saint Lucy's donkey flies!" he said sharply.

Our highly evolved domestic assistant shook her head indignantly. "What donkey? What's this Saint Lucy business?" she said. "Who's been filling your head with nonsense?"

"His mother and I have," Margherita answered. "As for nonsense, that's what you're talking right now. Keep quiet and find a little white bag for the crusts of bread, the bran, and the sugar cubes. Saint Lucy's donkey has to travel a long way and he'll be hungry."

"Unbelievable!" the girl exclaimed. "There are astronauts circling around the moon and still we have people filling children's minds with this sort of foolishness. There's no need to tell children fairy tales—on the contrary, they should be kept right on the railroad tracks of reality. The time for Saint Lucy and her donkey is over, and there's no more room for witches on brooms, or Santa Claus, or angels and devils. What's flying in the heavens today is communications satellites, interplanetary missiles, and astronauts. Only one thing is valid today: whatever can be explained by scientific reasoning!"

Margherita spread her arms wide in desolation. "I'm so sorry," she said mournfully. "I'm so sorry for God. Since He can't be explained through scientific reasoning He practically doesn't exist any more."

"I'm not talking about God!" Jo hedged. "I never once denied the existence of God."

"It's nice of you to let us continue believing in God," Margherita said with relief.

Jo stiffened. "Mrs. Guareschi, you have no call to make fun of me. I was talking specifically about children and what I said was that you shouldn't saturate their heads with stupid fantasies but should always try to keep them as close to scientific reality as possible. Only if you do that will there be a generation equipped to handle the future."

"Jo," I interrupted, "we already have enough champions for this new generation with its mind free of all stupid fantasy. We don't have very many of them here yet, but there are mobs of them in America, England, and the northern countries. And actually it's these beatniks or hippies or whatever you want to call them whose heads are saturated with stupid fantasies, to use your phrase, and don't have a spiritual life any more, which at least would allow them to escape from the frigid, comfortless reality of matter—instead they escape it using marijuana, LSD, and other hallucinogenic drugs. Too often their acid parties

degenerate into horrendous orgies and as just happened in
New York's Greenwich Village you have boys and girls
knifed to death or beaten to a pulp—you remember reading
about that fellow named 'Groovy' and the eighteen-year-old
heiress Linda."

"I don't see what those nightmares have to do with what
we were talking about," Jo said belligerently.

"But they *do*," I said, "because once upon a time young
people could avoid crude physical reality by falling back on
their spiritual reserves. Faith, hope, love, family, country, a
sense of responsibility, a desire to work, a sense of duty—
these were the drugs of young people in different times. And
they weren't hallucinogenic or poisonous!"

"With you, everything always turns into a tragedy!" the
girl protested. "What's drugs got to do with it? All I was
saying is that it's not necessary to deceive children by telling
them stories which don't exist in reality. It's damaging
because children then invent a false idea of the world and
later, when they realize they've been fooled, they suffer a
tremendous disillusionment. Try to be honest for a minute
and answer me: what did you feel, for instance, when the
most malicious little schoolmate of yours told you that the
gifts in your shoe weren't put there by Saint Lucy but by
your mother?"

"I'll be honest," I answered. "I hated that vicious little
fool and I hit him in the nose as hard as I could. Even so, I
refused to take what he said seriously. And today, fifty years
away from it, I always am consoled by those Eves of Saint
Lucy and the eager expectancy that kept me from falling
asleep right away like any other night. My heart still beats
faster when I think of how I'd wake up so early, leap out of

bed in the freezing cold room and run to open the window. I can still feel the same marvelous joy that I felt when I brought in my tiny boot from the windowsill, full of stuff. And the feeling of warmth that I had when I got back in between the covers and emptied out my boot. As I'm talking to you now I can feel that warmth and see all those wonderful presents that couldn't have cost more than a lira. Jo, our spiritual reserves are composed of comforting sensations linked to certain of our actions. When life seems hardest to us, bitterest, coldest, what a consolation it is to be able to feel again that soft, sweet warmth that thaws our old hearts and renews our strength and hope. Fifty years have passed and in this half-century I've learned a lot of ugly things, but I still believe in Saint Lucy and her little donkey. One time, when I was over thirty-five, I had to fill up Albertino's and Passionaria's shoes on Saint Lucy's Eve, and like a total idiot I asked my mother how she had managed to sneak into my room, open the window, fill my boot, close the window, and get out of there without my ever realizing. She looked at me, astonished and offended as she could be, and said angrily: 'I had absolutely nothing to do with it.' And I believed her."

Our domestic assistant was very amused. "Well then, why don't you test it? Why don't you put your shoe out on the windowsill tonight?"

"Because I'm afraid," I answered.

"Afraid of what?"

"Of finding it full of things in the morning."

"Just imagine!" the girl snorted. "Who in the world could crawl up there, to your pigeon coop?"

"You don't know what my mother's like," I said.

"But she's been dead for years!"

"That's what I mean. The dead can do anything. They can climb anywhere they want to."

"Don't make me laugh. You know perfectly well you'd find your shoe empty."

"Worse still to find it empty, because it would mean I haven't behaved myself during the last fifty years."

Jo was madly enjoying herself. "Now I understand. You don't dare do it because you're afraid of the supernatural!"

"Listen, girl, you'd better be afraid of it too," I answered. "One time a famous Communist was holding a council and pulled his watch out of his pocket and put it on the table in front of him. 'All right, God!' he thundered. 'I defy you. If you're up there, strike me down with a bolt of lightning! I'm giving you five minutes.' "

"Did he die?" Jo asked.

"He was assassinated many years later. God is never in a hurry."

Michelone came over and asked for a banana to give to Saint Lucy's donkey.

"Donkeys don't like bananas," I said.

"But I do," Michelone said.

This cast an entirely different light on things and I gave him the banana.

Slaves of the Dishwasher

☼

I just can't understand it," Jo said. "Prosperity has made its way into every house but this one."

This made me rather salty. "Certainly not. We don't yet have a powerboat, a caravan, a stereophonic record player, or a mobile made out of precious antiques. But I don't see why this gives you the right to say Prosperity hasn't entered our household."

"Prosperity doesn't mean merely to fill up your house with electrical appliances. Having a car and using it to smash your head against a tree or in a ditch isn't Prosperity. Just as it isn't Prosperity to have a superautomatic clothes washer and make use of it by filling the drum with plates, glasses, pots, and pans."

Strictly speaking, she was right, but in all fairness one should bear in mind that Margherita is allergic to anything mechanical, which includes can openers and corkscrews.

"To err is human," I said. "Anyway, since that disastrous episode you've always been in charge of the dishwasher and the washing machine."

"I've been in charge but I've been *irrationally* in charge, having to adapt myself to the irrationality of my present environment. That's why I'm saying Prosperity has yet to enter this household. Prosperity, when you come right down to it, can only result from the rational use of the machines Progress has put at our disposal."

"I don't get what you're driving at."

"It's a simple technical problem," she explained. "A washing machine and a dishwasher can only take one load at a time. A washing machine is useful and economical when it washes five kilos of laundry, a dishwasher when it washes the dishes used by five people. That is, five soup plates, five dinner plates, five fruit plates, five glasses, five cups and saucers, plus serving dishes, silver, and pots and pans."

"So?"

"So to obtain efficient use of your electrical appliances and not to become the slave of them, you have to adapt to the load capacity of each machine. You have to regulate the usage of linen, dishes, silverware, etc. etc. accordingly. As far as the dishwasher goes, ordinarily there are three of us— too few to make two loads daily for lunch and dinner, too many to do only one load after dinner. Therefore, what we have to do is program the loads . . ."

When I read or hear people talk about programming or high-level planning my insides get all twisted up. So I cut her off brusquely. "Jo, it's your problem. Do whatever you want about it."

Our conversation took place after dinner. The following morning, when I started to dry my face in the bathroom, I found in place of a towel a nice clean sheet. Naturally I began to roar like a bull. Jo appeared and asked what on earth was going on.

"Idle curiosity," I answered. "I'd be glad to know why in

God's name I have to use a sheet half the size of the town square instead of an ordinary, everyday towel to dry my face."

"Because an ordinary towel weighs 200 grams while a sheet weighs 1,500. And I need exactly 1,500 grams to complete the washing machine load for tomorrow. Use the sheet today and tomorrow morning, and then I'll give you an ordinary towel."

"But why should I dirty up half an acre of sheet instead of a towel?"

"That's modern programming for you," she said. "It's based on mathematical logic."

She was right so I dropped the subject.

At lunch Margherita ate her chopped chicken livers out of a soup bowl, while I had them in a fruit plate. Margherita had her steak on a regular dinner plate, but I ate mine out of a saucer and my vegetables came in another saucer. We ate our fruit compote out of coffee cups. The water came in ordinary glasses.

When we finished lunch, Jo explained her system. "This time we sacrificed him. But I've made up a rotating schedule. However you look at it, this way we only dirtied 2 soup plates, 2 dinner plates, 2 fruit plates, 2 coffee saucers, 2 coffee cups, and 3 glasses. Left for dinner, we have 3 soup plates for the minestrone, 3 dinner plates for the main course, 3 fruit plates for the vegetables, 3 coffee saucers for the pudding, and 3 coffee cups—2 for that vile mint purge you drink and 1 in which I'll have my wine, since we used 3 glasses for lunch and there are only 2 left for dinner. As to the bottom drawer of the dishwasher, we're all set, because we will have used just the right number of pots, pans, knives, forks, etc. etc."

"Absolutely brilliant," Margherita said. "But will you always be able to coordinate lunch with dinner?"

"That's my job. Don't worry about it," Jo answered.

"What if we were to invite somebody to luncheon?" Margherita inquired.

"Obviously in that case we would have to run 2 loads. Two loads will take care of 10 people. Therefore we can have 4 people at lunch. The 4 outsiders plus us 3 make 7, plus the 3 of us at dinner makes 10. One machine load after lunch takes care of 5 place settings. The 2 left over plus our 3 in the evening add up to the 5 for a night load."

"What if we invite people to dinner instead of lunch?"

"I'll study the problem and see how to program it."

"It seems like a perfect plan to me," I observed. "The trouble is that when you invite people over, you always offer them antipasto, fruit, dessert, different wines, coffee, liqueurs, and at least two courses. That throws everything off."

"I don't see why," Margherita answered. "All you have to do is run the machine more often."

"Naturally," I said. "But then you get involved in overtime—"

"I refuse to run more than two loads a day!" Jo declared. "You shouldn't put the worker at the mercy of the machine and make him its slave! If a machine has a limit to the load it can take, a worker can put up with just so much too. Times have changed and you've got to adapt. You have to be selective with your friends. He who finds a friend may find a treasure, as the saying goes; but it's a sight better to

lose a friend than to lose a domestic assistant. It will make
for a new society and a much improved one. Before you
begin dinner the hostess stands up and announces: 'In honor
of our charming guests, instead of serving antipasto, cheese,
desserts, various wines, and so on, we will have a simple
repast and give the difference in cost to CARE. You can
vary the donation, of course, and give to the victims of
whatever flood or avalanche is current."

"A noble idea," Margherita said approvingly. "But I
don't know about this fund-raising business. It's easy to
fund-raise billions of lire, but it's almost impossible to put
them into the right hands, because you never know whether
they're going to be properly distributed. I have a better
idea: Jo washes her share, and you and I will do the rest of
the dishes, Giovanni. You'll lend me a hand in running the
machine, won't you?"

Lending Margherita "a hand" means (seeing as God gave
me two hands) that it would be tiring and unmannerly of me
to work with one hand allowing the other to dangle uselessly.
And since two well-organized hands like mine lend themselves to doing a certain amount of work, there would be no
need for Margherita's two hands to enter the picture at all.
Therefore those very hands could go on working on the
historic pullover that will protect Michelone from the cold
when he goes into the Army.

"That's a good idea too," I said. "But let's not forget that
there's one electrical appliance among the many in our house
that would solve all problems in case we wanted to invite
people over to dinner, from preparing the meal right down to
washing the dishes and laundering the linen."

Jo looked at me, perplexed. "It sounds like the most complicated machine ever invented!"

"Not at all. What you have to do is dial a certain number and say, 'My name is So-and-So. For tomorrow at X o'clock reserve a table for X many people and serve us X, Y, and Z.' It's the only electrical appliance in the house that can solve the problems created by all the other electrical appliances."

"Very interesting," said Margherita. "I'd love to see how it works."

"I'm curious too," said Jo.

I made a phone call, and that night we dined at the restaurant, Margherita, Jo, and I.

Jo was very understanding that night. "Just for tonight," she said, "you may treat me as if I were your daughter or your niece. There are times when you bourgeois types have to make concessions to the proletariat, and there are times when we laborers must make concessions to the bourgeoisie."

Children Who Live
like Chickens

☼

Jo, who had her feet propped up and was leafing through her favorite weekly, sounded the alarm: "Phenomenon in sight with armed guard and baggage train!"

Margherita was at the courtyard window in a single bound, and since in serious households the husband must follow the wife, I followed Margherita.

Indeed, in spite of the flurries of white flakes, there the squadron was, making its way across the courtyard, which was already covered with half an inch of snow. The convoy was led by the Phenomenon propelled by the maternal motor, and the Phenomenon's father brought up the rear carrying a great cardboard box on one shoulder.

"They're insane," Margherita observed. "From their house here must be at least fifty meters. Crossing that windswept courtyard in a snowstorm is difficult and dangerous."

" 'Snowstorm' is such a tame word," Jo said with an edge of sarcasm. "I'd call it a 'blizzard'—it's more dramatic. It makes you think of the tragedy of people lost in the white wastes of the North Pole, of frozen hands and feet, of noses and ears that turn blue and disintegrate on contact."

Margherita was indignant. "A six-month-old baby is a tiny, fragile flower and a breath of air is enough to make her wilt. I resent your lightness about certain subjects. Besides, the chances are 99 out of a 100 that those two textbook examples of criminal negligence threw the baby into her carriage without a stitch on."

When the pram reached the breakfast room and was parked in front of a fire which by itself would have been enough to save Napoleon's troops during their disastrous flight from Russia, we all saw that the Phenomenon was quite a lot more than a mere baby—she looked like a whole sample-case of woolen goods.

"With all that wool on," I said stupidly, "I'm astonished she wasn't cooked on the journey over."

The Phenomenon was noticeably overheated but fortunately still raw. While Margherita fussed with the Phenomenon, Jo was fascinatedly watching the Phenomenon's father arranging the contents of the box he had carried over. When Jo saw him unpack a peculiar knot of shiny metal tubing and strong nylon netting, she gave a satisfied snort. "Ahah! I see the Phenomenon brought over a circus rig today. She must be warming up for a challenging, death-defying, breathtaking stunt if she needs that kind of safety net. True, yesterday's stunt was interesting, but it didn't send chills up your spine."

Margherita interrupted very resentfully and asked in a loud voice what could possibly send chills up the spine of a girl whose heart was already made of ice and whose brain was a computer with Milva's and the Beatles' biggest hits programmed in.

And this time I had to agree with Margherita, because the "stunt" performed by the Phenomenon the day before had been extremely significant and exciting. What the Phenomenon had done, entirely of her own accord and wholly unexpectedly, was to say "pew." And not just one time but eighteen times. Of course, the word in itself is not particularly exceptional. It was the way the Phenomenon had said it that was so exceptional. Eleonora Duse herself could not have said "pew" with such authority and dignity.

Meanwhile, the mysterious object had been rapidly assembled and it turned out to be one of those chicken coops marketed under the name "Baby-Box." The Phenomenon was deposited inside the Baby-Box so that we could observe her reactions. The result was disappointing. She not only disdained the thing, but in spite of persistent pleading from all of us, she absolutely refused to say "pew" again.

"The child is disoriented," Margherita pronounced. "Clearly the novelty of the environment has produced a minor psychological trauma in the child."

"Clearly the child is disgusted," Jo said. "And her psychological traumatization evidently derives from finding herself in a coop. Perhaps she doesn't relate to chickens well."

"You've got a point," Margherita said. "The fact that a baby only six months old knows that she's not a chicken denotes intelligence and exceptional precocity. Particularly when you consider that there are twenty- and thirty-year-old women who have not yet reached this stage of ideation and behave and think like chickens."

"Pretty pigsties, these modern inventions," Jo concluded, turning back to her weekly.

Once the Phenomenon was out of her sty and back in her pram free of the moist cloth covering her nether parts, she set to kicking happily and grabbing her feet to stick them in her mouth—a "stunt" that was ordinary enough but ever fascinating to us and absorbed all our attention so that we forgot Jo. Margherita and I, therefore, nearly jumped out of our skins when we heard Jo exclaim fiercely, "The time has come to destroy America!"

Apart from the fact that the United States is vastly important to the world balance of power, the idea of destroying a continent discovered by an Italian did not catch fire in my heart. So I asked Jo to explain this drastic pronouncement of hers.

"A country that invents such disgraceful mechanisms deserves total destruction," she said, standing up and spreading a magazine out in front of me. "Look here," she went on. "Now, as soon as a baby's born they toss him into a glass cage, naked as a worm, and they leave him there until he's a year old. All the mother does is look at some gauges and indicators and regulate the temperature, air conditioning, humidity, and so forth. If the baby dirties himself the mother presses a button and a jet of lukewarm water washes him—as if he were an automobile! Then a jet of hot air dries him off. The only annoyance is having to take the baby out of the cage to give him his formula in a bottle. If the baby starts crying, the thickness of the glass prevents you from hearing him and the mother goes on about her business. Now they're thinking about building enormous cages to contain hundreds of babies so they can be raised like the chickens in the Netherlands."

Margherita said she didn't see the point of the thing.

"It's very simple," Jo explained. "First, the babies breathe only filtered and sterilized air, they don't have to wear diapers. That means they can't be attacked by germs or get sick. Which in turn means that the mothers have all the time they could possibly need to compete in TV quizzes, to play bridge, to participate in political demonstrations, and to write long letters to Jackie Kennedy. In the meantime the baby grows healthy as a tinned sardine."

"The idea itself isn't bad," Margherita observed. "But they ought to build some large glass cages to put parents in who confine their children like that."

Jo went back to her reading and kept quiet for a little while. Then she blew up again. "We must destroy France!" she shouted.

Evidently Jo was in a genocidal mood that afternoon, and I didn't chastize her because every human being has his or her moments of weakness.

But Jo jumped up and waved still another magazine under my nose, pointing at a particular photograph. "Will you look at this picture and tell me what that French *maman* thinks she's doing, nursing a child and a lion cub at the same time!"

I looked but didn't say anything. Margherita, however, studied the picture and said, "If you ask me, I say it's lucky that French *maman* only has two distributors. Because if she had three, undoubtedly she'd nurse the child, the cub, and a calf."

Jo was wild with rage and said certain things about the

French mother that don't belong in a nice family book like this. I tried to calm her down. "Jo, you ought to try to remember that the French people are the most anti-racist people in the world and this Parisian mother gives us a striking demonstration that there should be no barriers of race in the world today, that every being in the animal world has a right to live."

"Wrong," the girl said. "I'd buy that if she was nursing a black or Oriental baby along with her own. But by nursing that lion cub she descends to the level of the beasts!"

"Jo," Margherita put in, "I'm not convinced by your process of reasoning. If by nursing that lion cub, the Frenchwoman descends to the level of beasts, would you say that the Roman Wolf, in nursing Romulus and Remus, descends to the level of woman?"

Jo was no fan of the Roman Wolf and could only growl, "To answer that question I'd have to be a wolf, not a woman."

Thus the second incident ended and Jo went back to her reading. Half an hour went by. Then Jo had her third blow-up.

"*Destroy Italy!*" she roared. "Look at this: in Cesena, a little girl nine years old is about to have a baby. That's so far beyond vileness it's almost unbelievable!"

"Jo," I said reasonably, "you're not recognizing the sportive side of the incident. We've seen Naples set the record for precocious maternity with a twelve-year-old mother. Then Catania beat Naples with an eleven-year-old mother. It was perfectly natural for healthy competition to set in among the various Italian regions. And here we have sunny, cheerful Romagna winning the race with a nine-year-old mother.

Remember that even though Naples is a wretchedly poor city, in the first two months of the soccer season the fans spent a billion lire to follow their team around on the tour. That's the way it is, Jo; when it comes to sports, the Italians don't care what it costs."

"Pew," said the Phenomenon decisively. And she had the last word.

A Lady Who Calls
Herself Mystery

That night after dinner, I was stretched out in my rocking chair to enjoy the fire warming our breakfast-room's hearth. A far more intelligent and amusing pastime than watching TV; healthier too, because heat and stretching out aid digestion, whereas the flickering ribbons of light in our picture-tube (teeny-screen) are difficult to decipher and to coordinate with the sound track, so they exhaust eyes, ears, brains, liver, and heart to the point where the digestive process is arrested so severely that often the consequences are fatal.

Jo was clearing the table and without warning barked at me, "The name of an exceptionally bright woman."

"Georgina!" suggested Margherita, who had just parked her half-century in the vicinity.

"Who's Georgina?" Jo asked.

"A girl *he* was madly in love with who instead of letting him marry her, jilted him for a much more interesting fellow."

"Quite so, she must have been exceptionally smart," Jo

admitted. "But she won't do because she's not a historic personage."

"Well then, Cleopatra!" Margherita suggested.

"A woman who kills herself isn't bright at all," Jo answered.

"Marie Curie," I exclaimed. "Nobel Prize in Physics."

"I don't want a scientist, I want a woman," Jo said.

"How about George Sand? A great French authoress who deserted her husband to go live with De Musset, Chopin, and many other important people."

"No good," the girl said. "She's got a man's name and besides, she's not popular."

"As far as her name goes," I answered, "the actress Dorian Gray also had a man's name. As far as being popular goes, it's not her fault that TV and the glossies didn't exist in her day. She'd be more famous than Elizabeth Taylor if she were alive today."

"What I want is the name of an Italian woman who is famous for her intelligence, her culture, and her beauty," Jo demanded.

"She doesn't exist," Margherita said positively. "To have the qualities you're looking for you need at least four women: one for beauty, one for culture, and two for intelligence."

"That's not true," I said. "The woman Jo is looking for did exist and is well known: Lucretia Borgia."

"The one who went around poisoning everybody?" the girl smirked.

"But that wasn't true," I said. "That's a myth invented by succeeding generations. Her contemporaries thought she was honest, beautiful, highly cultured, and very intelligent."

"In history her contemporaries don't matter a fig because they're all dead," Jo answered. "What matters is those of us who are alive. Lucretia Borgia just won't do. 'Mystery' is better."

"Do you mean to say that after you've had us wracking our brains to find the name of a famous woman, you're going to settle for 'Mystery'? A girl with a mind like yours is a menace to all God-fearing people."

"It's not my fault if you don't know the story. Anyhow, remember that you shouldn't judge people by their exteriors. A girl is not a box with 'Stewed Tomatoes' written on the outside and inside there are stewed tomatoes. There are girls that seem superficial but in fact have an intense interior life."

"Imagine that!" I laughed. "Let me tell you how many people would rather have an ingrown toenail than an intense interior life!"

"That's nice," Margherita said menacingly. "Only a man that's empty as a balloon won't admit that women have something inside."

"Margherita," I said worried. "Don't tell me *you* have an intense interior life too!"

"I *had* one," she said in a sad, distant voice. "But it's dead now."

"Of old age?"

"No, it was murdered! And *you* are the murderer!"

"Well put!" Jo approved loudly.

Naturally every story, to have a valid ending, ought to contain certain premises. Therefore I feel it's necessary to warn all twenty-three of my readers that, given the outright conformity on the part of all newspapers, the only part of the dailies that interests me at all are the letters to the editor.

The letter writers confide in the newspapers with boundless enthusiasm. They tell all, even the most intimate things. I remember reading in one of the most important dailies in Italy a letter in which a sixteen-year-old girl revealed that her parents, in order to punish her for her juvenile misdeeds, made her take down her panties, lie face down on a table, and then mama would press her fanny with a red-hot iron.

Why do people confide so freely in the newspapers?

In a world of masses seeking to compress and destroy the individual personality, in a world where success is not the logical consequence of universally recognized admirable qualities but rather is identical with notoriety, the common aspiration of all, young and old, is to stand out from the mass. A letter published in a daily or a magazine is read by millions of people. And even if the letter is signed with a pseudonym, the person who wrote it on seeing it published thinks of all the millions out there who are reading and worrying about His Case. They're talking about him, whether with approval or disapproval doesn't matter. He's come out of the mass, he's Somebody now.

This being so, it happened that one night, while I was reading the Parma daily, a strange letter caught my eye. "Mystery: I'm a young, pretty girl. By day I go to an honest but boring job. But by night I dress up in black pants and black turtleneck, go out carrying a Luger, and have myself a good time lighting fires in haylofts, burglarizing houses, and holding up the unfortunates that happen to cross my path. My life has been like this for years. Am I dreaming when I'm doing my honest job, or when I'm a firebug and a burglar? Am I the sweet, honest girl of the daytime or the criminal at night? Who am I?"

I read the anguished letter out loud to Margherita and concluded: "In my opinion, it's bad digestion. This girl should limit herself to milk-toast before she goes to bed at night."

Jo objected. "You're too quick about passing over people's psychological problems. I think the case is fascinating!"

"I agree," Margherita said. "She's obviously got a dual personality."

"Sure," I said. "A female Jekyll-and-Hyde."

"Don't be silly!" Jo shouted indignantly. "This is a fact, not a story. Here we have a woman who lives through a dream with such intensity that she doesn't know any more when she's dreaming or not. It's a horrifying question to have to ask yourself—'Who am I?' Isn't it tragic that the editor hasn't been able to find an answer for her?"

"Some editor!" Margherita was indignant. "How can he leave this poor girl to be torn to shreds by this terrible doubt?"

"He hasn't abandoned her," I said. "In this paper, it's the readers who answer. The editor picks the best answers."

In the next issue, the first answer to "Mystery" appeared: "I'm twenty-two and well built. Mystery's terrible problem has made me feel concerned and I'd like so much to be able to help this young pretty girl. I sleep very lightly and I'd be glad to put myself at her disposal to sleep with her and keep an eye open to find out whether this criminal business at night is dream or reality. Address inquiries to P.O. Box 768, Parma."

I read the answer out loud and Jo commented through clenched teeth, "What an ass!" Then she added, "Do you know what I'd do if I were this 'Mystery'? I'd write him a note and put it in a special envelope, bright red or yellow. Then I'd go over to the Parma post office and sit for a few hours the next day until somebody came out with my easily identifiable envelope. Then I'd slap his face but good!"

"I wouldn't," I answered. "If I were 'Mystery,' I'd bring the cognac bottle over here with three glasses and, along with the Mr. and Mrs., I'd toast the health of all young ladies who are so depraved as to write nonsense for the 'Letters to the Editor' columns of newspapers just to make themselves seem more interesting. That's what I'd do if I were 'Mystery.'"

Jo went to fetch the cognac. She brought back four glasses though. "As I don't know whether I'm on my day or my night routine," she explained, "I'd better give them both a drink."

We toasted all four of us.